INTRODUCTION TO THE MECHANICS
OF STELLAR SYSTEMS

INTRODUCTION TO
THE MECHANICS OF
STELLAR SYSTEMS

RUDOLF KURTH

Department of Astronomy
University of Manchester

PERGAMON PRESS

NEW YORK   LONDON   PARIS

1957

PUBLISHED BY

PERGAMON PRESS

122 East 55th Street, New York 22, N.Y.
4 & 5 Fitzroy Square, London, W.1
*24 Rue des Écoles, Paris V*e

Printed in Great Britain by John Wright & Sons Ltd.,
at The Stonebridge Press, Bristol

FOREWORD

THE present book has grown from notes of lectures given by the author at the Universities of St. Andrews, Bern and West-Berlin, and is intended to serve as an introduction for more advanced students. In writing it the author has tried to confine himself to matters which are reasonably well settled, and to bring out the essential parts of the subject. Little previous knowledge is required of the reader—not much beyond the elements of the differential and integral calculus and of analytical geometry. On the other hand the book does demand a certain willingness on the reader's part to think along with the author. Many of the examples are also intended to stimulate the reader into thinking critically.

Professor M. Schürer and Mr. U. Schwarz, both of Bern, have been so kind as to read and to comment on the German version of the text, the latter paying particular attention to the presentation, and both have made many a suggestion for its improvement. For all this help I express my best thanks once again both to them and to Dr. F. D. Kahn, of Manchester, who translated the text.

R. KURTH

CONTENTS

CHAPTER I

NATURAL STELLAR SYSTEMS

1. The structure of the Galaxy

1. Even a glance at the sky reveals two facts about our Galaxy, namely, that it has a flattened shape and that the Sun is in its interior. This follows at once because the Galaxy, as viewed from the Earth, looks like a stripe across the sky, with a central line which coincides very nearly with a great circle. The plane through this central line is called the Galactic plane.

A photographic study of the Milky Way shows a mass of other objects besides the numerous single stars (the "field stars"). The following are the most significant for our purpose.

(i) Bright and dark nebulosities, which demonstrate the existence of interstellar material in our Galaxy. Such material may also exist without being so obviously visible. Indirect methods of observation, which rely on interstellar absorption and reddening, are often useful here. The interstellar material is strongly concentrated towards the Galactic plane.

(ii) Clouds of stars. These are assemblies of stars having a cloud-like aspect. There are large clouds, rich in stars, in the constellations of Sagittarius and Scutum (with galactic longitudes $l = 335°$ and $350°$, respectively). (Galactic longitudes are directional coordinates in the Galactic plane; the angular coordinates in the perpendicular direction are called galactic latitudes. The north Galactic pole is in a direction perpendicular to the plane of the Galaxy and in the northern hemisphere, relative to the Earth. It has the equatorial coordinates $\alpha \approx 190°$, $\delta \approx 28°$, in the constellation Berenice. The direction $l = 0°$ is along the line of intersection of the plane of the Galaxy and the equatorial plane, and its equatorial coordinates are $\alpha = 280°$, $\delta = 0°$, in the constellation Aquila.)

(iii) Galactic stellar clusters (open clusters), which are subsystems, close to the Galactic plane and which show a loose structure, frequently of a spherical shape.

(iv) Globular clusters, which are strongly concentrated sub-systems, generally with spherical symmetry, and far outside the Galactic plane.

Finally, we may mention the radio noise which reaches us from the Milky Way, and whose intensity has a pronounced maximum in the direction $l \approx 325°$.

2. A first indication of the structure of our Galaxy is given by the apparent distribution in the sky of the globular clusters (there are about 100 known). The distribution is symmetrical with respect to the Galactic plane and is even approximately circularly symmetrical about the direction $l = 325°$ which lies in the plane (constellation of Sagittarius). This indicates that the globular clusters may be scattered with spherical symmetry about a centre whose direction has galactic longitude $l = 325°$. The most notable star clouds are, as we have seen, also situated in this direction, and so we arrive at the impression that the centre point of the assembly of globular clusters is the centre of our Galaxy. The fact that the Sun is far removed from the Galactic centre is shown by the overwhelming concentration of these globular clusters in the hemisphere about the direction $l = 325°$.

The approximately spherical character of the distribution of globular clusters was established by means of distance measurements using RR-Lyrae stars, which are abundant in the clusters, and which can be recognized by their rapid periodical fluctuations in intensity. (The periods are less than a day.) It is known that all these stars have about the same luminosity, which is fairly well determined. By measuring the apparent intensity of such a star its distance can be estimated by means of the inverse square law in empty space:

$$\text{intensity} = \text{luminosity}/4\pi \times \text{square of distance}.$$

Three results follow:

(i) The distances are such that the globular clusters must be members of the Galaxy.

(ii) Their distribution in space is, in fact, of spherical shape. The number of clusters per unit volume falls steadily from the centre of the distribution outwards.

(iii) The centre of the distribution is in the direction $l = 325°$, at a distance of about 8 to 10×10^3 parsec. The parsec (pc) is a convenient unit for the description of stellar systems, and equals 3.08×10^{18} cm. To give an impression of its length we note that a body moving at a speed of 1 km/s will cover a distance of 1 parsec in 10^6 years. The light year is another unit of length used in astronomy. This is the distance travelled by a light signal in empty space during one year, and 1 parsec $= 3.26$ light years.

We conclude, from the symmetrical distribution of globular clusters, that the Galaxy as a whole is a symmetrical structure. The spherical halo consisting of the different clusters envelops the strongly flattened main body. Its diameter is about 2.5×10^4 parsecs.

3. Further conclusions about the structure of our Galaxy have been drawn from statistical studies of the spatial distribution of stars. They are based on estimates of distances made by means of comparisons of light intensities with luminosities (in the same way as with RR-Lyrae stars). In the case of non-variable stars the luminosity may be estimated, for example, from the spectral type. The following results are significant for the mechanics of the system:

(i) The degree of flattening of the system varies with the spectral type of the stars considered. Those types which correspond to larger stellar masses show a greater concentration towards the plane.

(ii) It is shown by star counts, particularly those made with field stars of RR-Lyrae type, that the position of the greatest star density is also at the centre of the distribution of globular clusters ($l = 325°$, distance $\approx 9 \times 10^3$ pc). This point may therefore be regarded as the true centre of the Galaxy.

(iii) Looking in the opposite direction we reach the edge of our Galaxy at a distance of about 6×10^3 pc. The radius of the flattened part of the Galaxy is therefore about 15×10^3 pc. The distance of the Sun from the centre is thus about two-thirds of the radius of the disk.

(iv) The Sun is approximately in the central plane of the disk.

(v) The density of stars in the vicinity of the Sun is about one star per 10 pc^3.

(vi) The maximum thickness of the system is about 6×10^3 pc, roughly one-fifth of its diameter.

This is a provisional summary of the principal results. Other facts may occasionally be mentioned later.

2. The concept of a stellar system

We have up till now used the concept of a stellar system without explaining its meaning. With the observational material that we have discussed we shall now attempt a definition.

We define as a stellar system an assembly of stars which forms a unit in the sense that its members are neighbours in space, but are distant from all other stars. The motions of the member stars relative to one another, or relative to the mass centre of the system, are then, in a first approximation, determined by their mutual gravitation and by the interstellar material belonging to the system. Masses external to the system affect its *inner* motions only in higher orders of approximations, but, in general, they will affect considerably the motion of the system as a whole and, particularly, that of its mass centre. Investigations of motions of this type no longer belong to the mechanics of single systems but to the mechanics of a super-system, whose elements are single-star systems. The methods used for the study of single systems can also be applied in investigations of such super-systems.

An example is given by the globular clusters, which may be regarded as independent members, or sub-systems, of our Galaxy. They are apparently free from interstellar material and so the relative motions of stars in a cluster are, to the first order, determined by their mutual gravitation. To this order the cluster can be thought of as a stellar system. The gravitational effect of our Galaxy as a whole needs to be considered only in the second approximation. But if the Galaxy is regarded as a whole, then the cluster becomes an element of the super-system, which determines by its gravitation the motion of the cluster as a unit, or rather the motion of its centre of mass.

We aim to develop a mechanical theory of stellar systems, and it is desirable always to keep the real data in mind. We therefore give, in this introduction, a brief review of the properties of natural stellar systems, as far as we know them, and as far as it seems of interest for a mechanical theory. We shall continue the description of our Galaxy, and then go on to other stellar systems and super-systems, or at least to the most important of them.

3. The relative motions in our Galaxy

1. For an investigation of stellar motions in our Galaxy it is convenient to use a set of coordinates relative to which the system, as a whole, is at rest. It is tempting to fix these coordinates with the help of the globular clusters, for the central point of their distribution is also the centre of our Galaxy. The approximately spherical shape of their distribution allows us to assume that they have only a very slow systematic rotation, or none at all. (Strongly rotating systems are noticeably flattened. But a slow rotation is not excluded, because the disk-shaped main body of our Galaxy exerts a gravitational effect which opposes the flattening by rotation.) Individual clusters will, of course, be in motion, much as a swarm of flies remains at rest while each fly keeps moving.

To determine the motion of the Sun relative to the assembly of globular clusters one needs only to find the average of the relative motions of all the clusters, and then to reverse it. The large distances involved make their proper motions too slow to measure, but the radial velocities can be found, and these suffice to determine the solar motion. One finds, in this way, that the Sun has a velocity relative to the assembly of globular clusters, of about 200 km/s in the direction $l = 55°, b = 0°$. (The symbol b denotes galactic latitude; $b = 0$ is therefore the plane of the Galaxy.)

The direction of motion differs by 90° from the direction to the Galactic centre, or, in other words, the direction of motion is perpendicular to the radius. We deduce that the Sun moves, approximately, in a circle about the Galactic centre. Of course, quite different trajectories can also be reconciled with this observational result. But it does seem improbable that we should, just at this epoch, find ourselves at either the largest or the smallest distance from the centre during the description of a more general orbit of this type, as we should conclude from the observation of the 90° difference between the direction to the centre and the direction of motion. It is more plausible to regard the result not as the exceptional case but as the rule. If this is so, then the Sun must move along a circle.

The time of revolution of the Sun is easy to estimate, for it equals the quotient of the circumference of the orbit (about $2\pi \times 9000$ pc) and the linear speed (about 200 km/s). The period is 2 or 3×10^8 years, depending on the data used.

2. We now ask whether the other stars also move in circular orbits. We shall answer this question, in the first place, for the nearer stars, i.e. those whose distances are less than 100 or 200 pc. It is evident that stars with small velocities ($\ll 200$ km/s) relative to the Sun must move round the centre of our Galaxy in an orbit neighbouring to that of the Sun, that is, approximately along circles. Stars with larger relative motions will certainly not move along circular orbits. A more definite statement can only be made after a determination of the direction of the relative motion of the stars concerned.

The motion of the Sun relative to the assembly of the nearby stars can be found in a manner similar to that in which the motion relative to the assembly of globular clusters was determined. It appears that the Sun moves with a velocity of 20 km/s into the direction $l = 23°, b = 22^{\mathrm{d}}$ (constellation of Lyra) relative to the centroid of the system of neighbouring stars. Since 20 km/s is much less than 200 km/s, it follows that these stars also have, on the average, circular orbits about the centre of our Galaxy.

3. The mean motion of the nearby stars is now fixed and the question arises: How are the individual velocities distributed around the average?

It is found that

$$N \frac{1}{\sigma_1 \sqrt{(2\pi)}} \frac{1}{\sigma_2 \sqrt{(2\pi)}} \frac{1}{\sigma_3 \sqrt{(2\pi)}}$$
$$\times \exp\left[-\tfrac{1}{2}(v_1^2/\sigma_1^2 + v_2^2/\sigma_2^2 + v_3^2/\sigma_3^2)\right] \mathrm{d}v_1 \mathrm{d}v_2 \mathrm{d}v_3$$

is a good approximation to the number of stars whose random velocities lie in the (small) three-dimensional interval

$$v_1 \pm \tfrac{1}{2}\mathrm{d}v_1, \; v_2 \pm \tfrac{1}{2}\mathrm{d}v_2, \; v_3 \pm \tfrac{1}{2}\mathrm{d}v_3,$$

when suitable Cartesian axes are chosen. Here N is the number of stars considered, and σ_1, σ_2 and σ_3 are the root mean square dispersions of the velocity components in the three directions

(Schwarzschild's distribution law, 1907). In terms of arbitrary coordinates the number of stars in the interval is

$$\frac{N}{\pi^{\frac{3}{2}}}\sqrt{(\det\|a_{ij}\|)}\exp\left[-\sum_{i,j=1}^{3}a_{ij}v_iv_j\right]dv_1dv_2dv_3,$$

with a symmetrical matrix of coefficients $\|a_{ij}\|$. If v_1, v_2 and v_3 are regarded as orthogonal Cartesian coordinates of a three-dimensional space, the velocity space, then an ellipsoid (the velocity ellipsoid) is represented by the equation

$$v_1^2/\sigma_1^2 + v_2^2/\sigma_2^2 + v_3^2/\sigma_3^2 = 1,$$

viz. $$\Sigma a_{ij}v_iv_j = 1.$$

The table below gives data about its axes:

No. of the axis	Galactic longitude	Galactic latitude	R.M.S. dispersion
			(km/s)
1	345°	− 1°	28
2	255°	− 6°	20
3	81°	−84°	15

The figures are probably not very accurate. They are, for instance, found to depend on the choice of the stars used in their determination, and also vary considerably with spectral class. It appears, at first, that the galactic longitude of the v_1-axis differs considerably from that of the Galactic centre ($l = 325°$). For reasons of symmetry it would appear more likely that one axis of the velocity ellipsoid should point towards the Galactic centre, and theory supports this expectation (cf. V, § 3). But the standard error in the determination of l is about 10°, and so it is not possible to decide how much of the 20° difference is due to inaccurate observation, and how much to a genuine discrepancy in direction.

Schwarzschild's law does not apply to stars with large random speeds $\{v = \sqrt{(v_1^2 + v_2^2 + v_3^2)} > 60 \text{ km/s}\}$. There are considerably more such stars than the law predicts, and their directions of motion are almost always into the hemisphere with the mean coordinate $l = 235°, b = 0°$. This is exactly opposite to the direction of rotation $l = 55°, b = 0°$. We conclude that these so-called "high-velocity stars" are really low-velocity stars. They move, on the average, in the direction of the general rotation with speeds below 140 km/s. The orbits of individual stars therefore deviate considerably from circular orbits, and such stars will approach relatively close to the Galactic centre.

4. The above results apply to stars in the near neighbourhood of the Sun. The following empirical regularities are found when the mean motion of these stars is compared with the mean motion of other groups of stars occupying relatively small volumes of space. If such a group lies in the Galactic plane then its radial velocity $\bar{R}$ relative to the stars in the solar neighbourhood is given by
$$\bar{R} = \text{const.} \sin 2(l - l_0),$$

and the average proper motion is
$$\bar{\mu} = \text{const.} \cos 2(l - l_0).$$

In these formulae l is the mean galactic longitude of the group considered and l_0 a constant longitude. According to observations $l_0 = 325°$ or $145°$ (two directions are possible), and these values give the directions towards and away from the Galactic centre. The amplitude of the "double-wave" in the radial velocities $\bar{R}$ depends on the distance from the Sun to the group of stars: at a distance of 500 pc it is of the order of 10 km/s. The amplitude of the double wave in proper motions is of the order of a few thousandths of a second of arc per annum.

There is an additional constant term, of the order of a few km/s, in the radial velocities of stars of spectral types O and B. The term seems to depend on the distance, and decreases quite rapidly to zero for more distant stars.

4. Clusters of stars

We consider, first of all, the globular clusters. Their diameters are scattered around an average of about 70 pc. It has not yet been possible to determine directly the number of stars within them, for the clusters are so very distant that only the brightest stars may be observed, while the multitude of dimmer stars remain invisible. The bright stars tend to concentrate so strongly towards the centre that no one has yet photographically resolved he nucleus of a cluster into single stars. Counting will therefore nly yield a lower limit for the true stellar abundances. These mits go up to 7×10^4 stars (in the cluster M22). A lower limit o the average star density is therefore 0·06 stars per pc³. This s 35 times the density of stars of comparable luminosity in the icinity of the Sun. The stellar densities in the clusters seem to ecrease as r^{-3}, r^{-4} or $e^{-r \cdot \text{const}}$, where r is the radial distance from he centre.

Interstellar material has not been found in any cluster.

Several clusters are not strictly spherical but show a definite lattening, which indicates rotation. The radial velocities relative o the Sun of stars in clusters have a dispersion smaller than 0 km/s about their average, which itself gives the radial velocity f the cluster as a whole. The radial velocities of clusters, on heir part, have a dispersion of about 100 km/s about their verage (which is the reverse of the solar motion).

Galactic clusters have diameters lying between 2 and 6 pc, and isually contain a few hundred stars. The average density of tars is between 0·2 and 83 stars per pc³. The radial velocities of ndividual stars have a dispersion of about 1 km/s about the iverage. Galactic clusters are much less centrally condensed than ;lobular clusters. They contain interstellar material.

Globular and open clusters are therefore different in almost very respect. They have different distributions in space, different iizes and numbers of stars, different structures and concentra-,ions, their motions differ, and interstellar material is absent in ne group and present in the other. Finally, the spectral types f the component stars are different, but we shall not enter into his question here.

5. The extra-galactic nebulae

1. Besides the stellar systems we have discussed there is another :lass of systems which we have not mentioned, although it is by ar the most extensive, namely, the class of extra-galactic nebulae or "spiral nebulae". These, however, are not really nebulosities but stellar systems like our Galaxy. The similarity follows from a series of analogies between our Galaxy and the external galaxies, particularly from their distances and sizes. These measurements are estimated in a similar way as those of globular clusters, and

linear dimensions are obtained which are comparable with thos
of our Galaxy. Their distances from each other are about 10 c
20 times their diameters.

The galaxies are divided, according to shape and structure
into the two main classes of regular and irregular systems. Th
regular galaxies are further divided into elliptical and spira
systems, and these in turn into ordinary and barred spirals
Following Hubble the regular galaxies are arranged into th
following sequence.

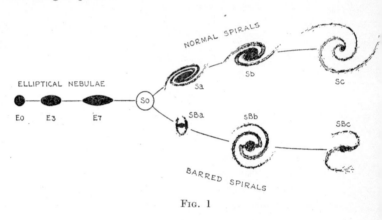

Fig. 1

The numbers in the descriptions of the elliptical nebulae (E
denote the degree of flattening. Systems of type E0 are no
flattened, but are spherical, while systems of type E7 show th
largest flattening which occurs, and which corresponds to a
axial ratio 3 : 1. The linear diameters increase along the sequenc
from E0 to S(B)c and so do the relative abundances, relate
classes like Sa and SBa being regarded as one. The total luminosi
ties seem to have about the same upper limit for all regula
systems. One may, perhaps, conclude from this that there is
common upper limit to the number of stars and to the total mass
Recently there has been a tendency to believe that there ar
many dwarf galaxies with much lower masses and luminosities.

There is much interstellar material in the irregular and spira
nebulae, but none in the elliptical systems.

The occurrence of stars with spectral types O and B and o
interstellar material is characteristic of the arms of spiral nebulae

It appears that in our Galaxy the O and B stars and the inter-stellar material are also arranged in spirals, so that our system must be regarded as a spiral nebula. However, it seems that the deviation from rotational symmetry is only small.

There must be rotation present in the flattened systems, which are in the great majority. In the case of a few systems the law of rotation has been quantitatively deduced from radial velocity measurements. Two important results are given in the following two diagrams.

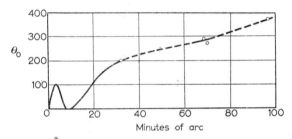

Fig. 2 Spiral Nebula M31, Type Sb (Andromeda).

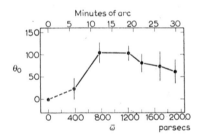

Fig. 3 Spiral Nebula M33, Type Sc.

Observational difficulties have so far made it impossible to decide whether the convex or the concave side of a spiral arm precedes during the rotation. The decision is not easy to make in the case of our Galaxy, where those parts of the spiral arms which have been plotted seem to lie close to a circle about the Galactic centre. It is therefore not clear, because of observational errors, whether the arms are opening out or winding up. The general opinion seems to be that the convex side of an arm precedes, and the arms are winding up.

2. So far we have dealt only with single or "field" galaxies. But we know that there are binary and multiple stars as well as star clusters in our Galaxy, in addition to the single or "field" stars. In the same way there are assemblies among the stellar systems, such as double and multiple systems, "groups" of galaxies (with a membership of order ten) and clusters of galaxies (with a membership of larger order of magnitude). Our Galaxy belongs to the so-called local group, which seems to have at least thirteen members.

Some tens of thousands of clusters are known. There are, in general, between a hundred and a thousand galaxies in each. The transition from groups to clusters is continuous. Counts of galaxies give only lower limits, as in the case of globular clusters, since small and dim systems, which may be present, may remain undetected. The linear diameters of clusters are of the order of 10^6 pc. The distribution of the galaxies in these super-systems resembles the distribution of stars in open clusters. The radial velocities are scattered about the average with a dispersion of about 800 km/s.

3. The clusters can be regarded as local condensations in the assembly of all the galaxies, which has the following properties.

In spite of considerable local fluctuations it seems that galaxies are, on the whole, uniformly distributed in observable space. Their number density lies between 5 and 10 per cube of side 10^6 pc. In almost all cases there is a red shift in the line spectra, which seems to be proportional to the distances from our Galaxy. (The contribution due to the solar motion with respect to our Galaxy must first be removed.) If the red shift is interpreted as being due to the Doppler effect, then we have the formula for the average radial velocity $\bar{R}$ of galaxies at a distance r

$$\bar{R} = Kr,$$

where K is a constant.

K has the dimensions of reciprocal time and is measured in units of km/s^{-1} pc^{-1}. While it is not desirable to have two units of length we do wish to keep the unit km/s as being easily visualized. We therefore recall that, to within 2 per cent,

$$1 \text{ km/s} = 1 \text{ pc}/10^6 \text{ years.}$$

If we choose, as unit, a time interval of 10^6 years (1 Z for short), then we have, to a good enough approximation,

$$1 \text{ km/s} = 1 \text{ pc}/Z.$$

With these units (pc and Z)

$$K \approx 10^{-4}[Z^{-1}].$$

Very large radial velocities are observed, up to one-fifth the speed of light. The question has therefore been repeatedly asked whether the red shift can reliably be interpreted as an indication of motion; might there not be a physical effect (unknown as yet) which could give rise to the reddening? We return to this question in V, § 5.7.

6. Summary

We have met four fundamental types in our survey of stellar systems:

(1) Clouds (star clouds, irregular stellar systems).
(2) Spirals (galaxies).
(3) Ellipsoids (galaxies, some globular clusters).
(4) Spheres (star clusters, galaxies, clusters of galaxies).

Galactic clusters may be regarded as a transitional stage between clouds and spheres. The spirals and ellipsoids are in rotation and consequently possess angular momentum, which vanishes very nearly for the spheres. On the other hand the clouds may or may not rotate; both possibilities are conceivable. The ellipsoids are related kinematically to the spirals and geometrically to the spheres.

There appears to be considerably more interstellar material in the clouds and the spirals than in the ellipsoids and spheres. In this sense the Galactic clusters resemble the clouds rather than the spheres.

One may differentiate between two stellar populations, that is to say, two types of composition of a system by stars of different spectral types. Population I is characteristic of

  (i) the solar neighbourhood,
 (ii) irregular galaxies,
(iii) arms of spiral systems,
(iv) Galactic clusters.

Population II is characteristic of

(i) the system of high-velocity stars in the solar neighbour-hood,

(ii) the nuclei of spiral systems,

(iii) elliptical galaxies,

(iv) globular clusters.

O and B stars, by whose distributions in space the spiral structure of our Galaxy was recognized, are typical members of population I. The fact that the high-velocity stars belong to population II, the population of the Galactic nucleus, fits in with the conclusion (§ 3.3 above) that their orbits take them close to the Galactic centre.

Our selection of the fundamental types of clouds, spirals, ellipsoids and spheres, seems to be natural, not only from the geometrical point of view, but also from the point of view of state of motion, of the presence of interstellar material and of stellar population. The star clouds in the Galactic centre seem, however, to be exceptional in this last respect, for they belong to population II, although all clouds should belong to population I according to our ordering. The other cloud-like structures, the irregular galaxies, actually do belong to population I.

Examples

1. How is the inverse square law of light intensity generalized to apply to non-empty space?

2. What is the effect of the presence of interstellar material on distance measurements which are based on the inverse square law?

3. Describe the apparent distortion of the system of globular clusters which occurs when the presence of interstellar absorption in the Galactic plane is neglected.

4. How can interstellar material bring about reddening of starlight? Does it necessarily bring it about?

5. Discuss, in detail, the means by which the velocity of the Sun can be found relative to the assembly of the nearby stars.

6. How far are the two versions of Schwarzschild's law, given in the text, equivalent to one another?

7. Use Schwarzschild's law to derive the distribution of speeds of stars. Discuss this distribution under the simplifying assumption that the velocity dispersions are equal in all directions.

8. Why do the high-velocity stars approach relatively close to the Galactic centre during a description of their orbits?

Comments on the Literature

I have not attempted to give a complete set of references but have, rather, tried to indicate those parts of the literature which I have found most useful, in the hope that I might, in this way, help the student in his choice of further reading matter. Reference to, or omission of, a particular work implies no judgment on its value.

The data in this chapter are, for the most part, taken from:

[1] BECKER, W., *Sterne und Sternsysteme*, Dresden and Leipzig, 1950. This book is invaluable to research workers for its wealth of facts, points of view, data and references. It also serves as a first introduction to practical astrophysics, stellar statistics and dynamics, and cosmology. The presentation is elementary and it makes easy reading.

A convenient collection of data is to be found in:

[2] LANDOLT-BÖRNSTEIN, *Zahlenwerte und Funktionen aus Astronomie und Geophysik*, Berlin-Göttingen-Heidelberg, 1952.

The methods by which the data are found are extensively described in the following books:

[3] TRUMPLER, R. J., and WEAVER, H. F., *Statistical Astronomy*, University of California Press, 1953.

[4] V. D. PAHLEN, E., *Lehrbuch der Stellarstatistik*, Leipzig, 1937.

[5] SMART, W. M., *Stellar Dynamics*, Cambridge, 1938.

Trumpler and Weaver's seems to be an excellent textbook. v. d. Pahlen's work is more like a handbook, to judge by its size and nature. It attempts to describe objectively the various researches, without evaluating their relevance. Smart's book is similar. Its many references, particularly to older literature, are helpful.

These last two books can be used to advantage in the discussion of particular problems. A first introduction to the methods is also found in Becker's book [1].

For radio astronomy we may mention:

[6] LOVELL, A. C. B., and CLEGG, J. A., *Radio Astronomy*, London, 1952.

[7] PAWSEY, J. L., and BRACEWELL, R. N., *Radio Astronomy*, Oxford, 1955.

A brief survey is given by:

[8] WALDMEIER, M., *Radiowellen aus dem Weltraum*, Zürich, 1954.

Note to § 3.3. Fricke has recently cast doubt on the validity of the ellipsoidal distribution of velocity components in the solar neighbourhood:

[9] FRICKE, W., *Die Naturwissenschaften*, **38**, 438–448, 1951.

CHAPTER II

SKETCH OF A MECHANICS OF STELLAR SYSTEMS

1. In the previous chapter we have summarized briefly, and in a simplified fashion, the observational facts about the present mechanical state of stellar systems. Before constructing a theory we must, however, decide what its objectives are to be. We therefore ask:

   (i) On which laws are we able, or compelled, to base the mechanics of stellar systems?

  (ii) How shall the laws be formulated and applied?

 (iii) What do we expect the theory to tell us?

2. The validity of Newtonian mechanics will be the basic assumption in the development of the theory. In particular we shall postulate the validity of

   (i) the law of conservation of mass,

  (ii) Newton's equations of motion,

and (iii) Newton's law of gravitation.

In general we shall neglect the influence of interstellar material. For some stellar systems, though not for all, this seems to be justifiable. But we are forced to do so by the insurmountable mathematical difficulties which are introduced when the influence of interstellar matter is taken into account. The mathematics is hard, in any case. A further difficulty is the scarcity of observational data.

It would, of course, be possible to attempt a relativistic mechanics of stellar systems, but there seems to be no call for it, as long as the simpler Newtonian theory has not been fully developed and tested.

3. How can we, and how shall we, formulate and apply these basic assumptions? The following are the models which seem to be at all possible:

(i) We represent the real stellar system by an assembly of n gravitating particles, where $n \gg 1$; this is the point of view of celestial mechanics.

(ii) We represent the real system by a material continuum, streaming in a 6-dimensional phase space. This leads to stellar dynamics, in the restricted sense.

(iii) We represent the real system by a particle and continuum model. To do so we define continuous probability distributions for the positions and states of motion of discrete particles, and then evaluate and interpret them. This is a statistical mechanics of stellar systems.

All three approaches have their own limitations.

The first approach requires an accuracy which the problems do not justify. We do not wish to know, for instance, the particular positions of individual stars and their particular states of motion, but only their total number, and their distribution among the different states of motion. We can, therefore, make use of only the most general results concerning the development of a gravitating n-body system.

The second approach neglects the interaction between each pair of stars, but lets the motion of an individual star be determined by a smoothed-out gravitational force due to the whole system. In this way we lose one of the characteristics of the real system, and the model can be regarded, at most, as a useful approximation for a limited, not too large, interval of time.

There seem, at first, to be no objections to a statistical mechanics of stellar systems. However, we shall try to apply it in Chapter VI, and shall find difficulties even in the basic formulation of the problem which appear to be insurmountable. The gravitational forces are not sufficiently powerful to ensure the continued existence of the system under all circumstances. But such a continued existence in a definite volume of space, whether brought about by internal or external forces, is a fundamental requirement of statistical mechanics.

In the following chapter the three basic approaches are discussed one by one.

4. What do we really want the theory to tell us? The *first fundamental question* to be answered by a mechanical theory is

this: The mechanical state of a given stellar system is supposed to be known at an arbitrary time $t = 0$. What will be its mechanical development? The mechanical state of the system at any instant is determined by the positions and the velocities of the stars at that instant.

This question can be interpreted in two ways:

(i) How can the development of the system be calculated?

(ii) How can it be described without an explicit calculation?

These two subsidiary questions differ in their mathematical character. The first refers to the neighbourhood of the point $t = 0$ on the time axis, and belongs to the "analysis in the small". The second refers to the behaviour of the system along the *whole* time axis and this is "analysis in the large". Explicit calculations are generally possible only for limited intervals of time, so that we must attempt to make the description without using a formal or numerical calculation. In classical celestial mechanics the determination of orbits corresponds roughly to the first question, while the problem of the stability of the planetary system corresponds to the second.

The most significant data about the initial states of real systems have been summarized in Chapter I. But they are in no case sufficiently accurate or extensive for us to deduce the present mechanical state of any individual stellar system. We must therefore make some more or less plausible assumption, either about the present state as a whole, from the available data, or about the state of the system just after the formation of the stars. The latter would be a cosmogonic hypothesis, and it is evident that there are serious objections to such a method.

On the other hand a cosmogonic hypothesis seems to offer the only possibility of obtaining an answer to the *second fundamental question*: How can we explain the present state of real systems? Because the state at time $t = 0$ and the line of evolution through that time determine one another uniquely, we may ask instead how we can understand why the system follows a particular line of evolution.

The following answers seem possible, bearing in mind the observational results.

The first answer is purely mechanical, and it states that possibly, the lines of evolution through all the conceivable initial states eventually converge to the same final state. After a sufficiently long period the individual lines of evolution lose their characteristics and become practically indistinguishable.

The second answer is also mechanical, but to some extent opposed to the first: Individual systems follow approximately periodical and mutually similar cycles of states. (In this case the influence of interstellar material must certainly be neglected.) The real systems are, at any instant, distributed randomly among the different states of the "average" cycle.

Both answers have this in common that they seek the explanation of the law of evolution solely in the mechanical equations of motion and eliminate (or neglect) the peculiarities of the "initial state" in which the system came into being. The third answer, on the other hand, gives a considerable significance to the initial states. According to it the mechanical history of the system is decisively influenced by its physical prehistory.

The particular problems are, in the case of the first and second answers, to establish the existence of limiting states and of cycles, to describe these more closely and to compare them, finally, with the states of real systems. In the case of the third approach we must invent a physical hypothesis about the initial state and go on to deduce the mechanical development of the system up to its present state.

In any case the different approaches are not mutually exclusive. The following combination is possible, for example. Very markedly different initial lines may diverge from the various physico-mechanical initial states and then eventually converge towards one or a few final states. These have at present been attained by only some of the real stellar systems (perhaps by the ellipsoidal and spherical ones). Short-period cyclical changes in state, with small amplitudes, are superposed on this secular evolution and also on the final states.

It is, perhaps, permissible to suppose that this is the model closest to reality, possibly in the following way. Giant clouds of diffuse material condense into stars and therefore into irregular stellar systems. Under the influence of the remaining interstellar material and of gravitation these will tend to assume progressively more regular shapes, first spirals, later ellipsoids and spheres, owing to the continued contraction and the consumption of interstellar material.

These mental pictures are all very vague. We are still far from an answer to our two basic questions and are certainly not in any position to construct a consistent mechanics of stellar systems. For the present we can do little more than to make a plan of a theory, to relate it to the sum total of our astronomical knowledge, as we have attempted to do in the previous chapter, and then to fashion its individual parts and test them. This will be done in the following chapters.

In the discussions so far we have treated the stellar systems as though they were completely independent of one another. This is not, in fact, true. The problems which arise from the interaction of stellar systems have hardly been considered up to the present time.

Example

A star of luminosity L loses energy at a rate of L erg/s and therefore, according to Einstein's mass-energy relation, loses mass at a rate L/c^2 g/s (the symbol c denotes the speed of light). For how long a period may the mass of a star be considered to be effectively constant, assuming that L remains constant? Take $c = 3 \times 10^{10}$ cm/s, and, for the Sun, take $L = 4 \times 10^{33}$ erg/s and the mass $\odot = 2 \times 10^{33}$ g.

Literature

Camm has recently given a very clear summary of the present state of stellar dynamics:

CAMM, G. L., "Recent Developments in Stellar Dynamics", in *Vistas in Astronomy*, Vol. 1, London and New York, 1955.

CHAPTER III

MECHANICS OF SYSTEMS OF MASS-POINTS

1. Newton's law of motion

1. The classical mechanics of systems of mass-points is the foundation for the mechanics of stellar systems. We shall summarize the most relevant parts of it in this chapter.

A mass-point (or particle) is defined as a body whose linear dimensions are small compared to those of the system. Occasionally a stricter definition is required, for instance when the forces acting on the body depend on its shape and inner structure. This happens when the body moves through a resisting medium such as interstellar material. We shall also require a particle to be spherically symmetrical.

Consider now a system of n particles, defined by the subscripts $1, 2, ..., n$. The ith particle has mass m_i, its vector coordinate in terms of orthogonal Cartesian axes is r_i and it is acted on by a force k_i. Differentiation with respect to time will be denoted by a dot. Newton's law of motion then states that a set of axes can be chosen such that the accelerations of the particles are given by the equations

$$m_i \ddot{r}_i = k_i, \qquad i = 1, 2, ..., n.$$

We shall in future always assume that such a set of axes has been chosen.

The forces k_i in general depend on the positions of all the particles. If they depend only on these the system is called mechanically closed. But the forces may, in addition, be functions of the instantaneous velocities $\dot{r}_i$, of the time t and of any other type of physical quantity.

Let us consider more closely the important case in which the forces are determined solely by the relative positions of the particles, in addition to the time variable t. The forces are then functions of the difference vectors $r_i - r_j$ alone, so that, for example,

$$k_1 = k_1(r_1 - r_2, r_1 - r_3, \dots; t), \quad \text{etc.}$$

Now define a new set of Cartesian axes parallel to the previous set and let a be the constant velocity of the origin of the new set relative to that of the old. Let b be a constant vector and r_i' the position vector of the ith particle in the new system of axes, then

$$r_i = r_i' + at + b.$$

If these expressions are inserted into the Newtonian equations of motion, then

$$m_i \ddot{r}_i' = k_i(r_1' - r_2', r_1' - r_3', \dots; t).$$

It follows that the equations of motion are invariant to a uniform translation of the coordinate system under these conditions.

2. We shall now try to choose the coordinate system which gives the simplest description of the motions.

The following results evidently hold for gravitational forces, with which we have to deal, to a large extent, in the mechanics of stellar systems. The resultant force on each particle is the vector sum of the single forces due to the other particles. Thus, for the first particle,

$$k_1 = k_{12} + k_{13} + \dots \quad + k_{1n}, \quad \text{etc.}$$

Apart from the masses of i and j the force k_{ij} depends only on relative positions of i and j, so that

$$k_{ij} = k_{ij}(r_i - r_j).$$

At every instant k_{ij} is equal and opposite to k_{ji} so that

$$k_{ij}(r_i - r_j) = -k_{ji}(r_j - r_i).$$

It follows that the sum of all the forces k_i equals zero. For every term k_{ij}, occurring in the expression for k_i, goes out with the corresponding term k_{ji}, in the expression for k_j. Following Newton's laws the sum of the products of masses and accelerations is zero, and so

$$\sum_{i=1}^{n} m_i \ddot{r}_i = 0, \quad \text{for all } t.$$

Two successive integrations give that, at time t,

$$\sum_{i=1}^{n} m_i \dot{r}_i = a$$

and
$$\sum_{i=1}^{n} m_i r_i = at + b,$$

where a and b are arbitrary constant vectors of integration.

The expression $m_i \dot{r}_i$ is called the momentum of the ith particle. The sum of all the momenta is therefore constant in time. This is the law of conservation of momentum.

The vector a can be eliminated from the second equation by means of the first. We then obtain another sum which is completely determined by the instantaneous positions and velocities of the individual particles and which is constant in time, namely

$$\sum_{i=1}^{n} m_i(r_i - \dot{r}_i t) = b.$$

We define as the centroid (or centre of gravity) of the system the point with the vector coordinate r_*, such that

$$r_* = \frac{1}{M} \sum_{i=1}^{n} r_i m_i,$$

where
$$M = \sum_{i=1}^{n} m_i,$$

and denotes the total mass of the system. The equation

$$\sum_{i=1}^{n} m_i \ddot{r}_i = 0$$

therefore leads to
$$M\ddot{r}_* = 0,$$
$$M\dot{r}_* = a,$$
$$Mr_* = at + b.$$

The final equation expresses the theorem of the centroid, which states that the centroid of the system is in uniform motion. But Newton's laws of motion are invariant with respect to uniform translations. It is tempting to simplify the description of the motions by choosing the coordinate system to be at rest relative to the centroid.

c

We thus define a new set of axes, with its origin at the centroid, so that the new coordinates are given by

$$r' = r - r_*.$$

Newton's laws apply to the new axes so that

$$m_1 \ddot{r}'_1 = k_1(r'_1 - r'_2, \ldots r'_1 - r'_n).$$

A result concerning the motion of the centroid can be found even when the forces in the system do not add up to zero. For from

$$m_i \ddot{r}_i = k_i$$

there follows that

$$\sum_{i=1}^{n} m_i \ddot{r}_i = \sum_{i=1}^{n} k_i$$

or

$$M \ddot{r}_* = \sum_{i=1}^{n} k_i.$$

The centroid moves as though it were a particle with a mass equal to that of the whole system, acted upon by the sum of all the forces.

3. The gravitational force k_{ij} between two particles acts along the line joining them. In vectorial notation this may be written

$$(r_i - r_j) \times k_{ij} = 0.$$

(Vector multiplication is denoted by the symbol $\times$.) We define the product $r_i \times (m_i \dot{r}_i)$ as the angular momentum of the ith particle, and the result below follows easily. The sum of all the angular momenta

$$M = \sum_{i=1}^{n} r_i \times m_i \dot{r}_i$$

remains constant in the system. This is the law of conservation of (total) angular momentum.

The law will be proved by calculating the time derivative of M and showing that it vanishes. Differentiation yields, first, that

$$\dot{M} = \sum_{i=1}^{n} r_i \times m_i \ddot{r}_i;$$

ith the aid of Newton's laws of motion

$$\dot{M} = \sum_{i=1}^{n} r_i \times k_i$$

$$= \sum_{i=1}^{n} \sum_{j \neq i} r_i \times k_{ij}$$

$$= \sum_{i=1}^{n} \sum_{j=1}^{n} r_i \times k_{ij},$$

here the forces $k_{ii} \equiv 0$ have been introduced formally. Changing he order of summation, we have

$$\dot{M} = \sum_{j} \sum_{i} r_j \times k_{ji}$$

$$= - \sum_{j} \sum_{i} r_j \times k_{ij}.$$

We add this to the first equation for $\dot{M}$ to find

$$2\dot{M} = \sum_{i} \sum_{j} (r_i - r_j) \times k_{ij} = 0,$$

id this is the required result.

4. We now come to the last conservation law, that of energy. he gravitational forces have a potential, as we shall demonstrate . IV, § 1.1. This means that there exists, for any gravitating ystem, a function

$$U = U(r_1, r_2, ..., r_n)$$

f the position vectors

$$r_i = \begin{pmatrix} x_i \\ y_i \\ z_i \end{pmatrix}, \qquad i = 1, 2, ..., n,$$

hich is such that the forces

$$k_i = \begin{pmatrix} X_i \\ Y_i \\ Z_i \end{pmatrix}, \qquad i = 1, 2, ..., n,$$

may be expressed as negative gradients of U

$$\left. \begin{aligned} X_i &= -\frac{\partial}{\partial x_i} U(x_1, \dots, z_n), \\ Y_i &= -\frac{\partial}{\partial y_i} U(x_1, \dots, z_n), \\ Z_i &= -\frac{\partial}{\partial z_i} U(x_1, \dots, z_n). \end{aligned} \right\}$$

The function U is called the potential of the system, or of the forces k_i; its numerical value for any configuration of the position vectors $(r_1, \dots, r_n)$ is called the potential energy of the system in that configuration. The negative gradient (rather than a positive one) is introduced in accordance with the general convention.

Newton's laws of motion are now

$$m_i \ddot{x}_i = -\frac{\partial U}{\partial x_i}, \quad \text{etc.}$$

Suppose that a system has a potential which does not depend explicitly on the time variable t, then the law of the conservation of energy states: The mechanical system has an "energy function"

$$H \equiv \tfrac{1}{2} \sum_{i=1}^{n} m_i \dot{r}_i^2 + U(r_1, \dots, r_n),$$

which retains the same value for all time when the solutions of the equations of motion are substituted for the vectors r_i.

The proof again consists in showing that the time derivative of the energy function is zero. One obtains that

$$\dot{H} = \sum_i \left(m_i \dot{r}_i \cdot \ddot{r}_i + \frac{\partial U}{\partial x_i} \dot{x}_i + \frac{\partial U}{\partial y_i} \dot{y}_i + \frac{\partial U}{\partial z_i} \dot{z}_i \right)$$

$$= \sum_i (m_i \ddot{r}_i - k_i) \cdot \dot{r}_i \equiv 0.$$

The expression $\tfrac{1}{2} m_i \dot{r}_i^2$ is called the kinetic energy of the ith particle, and the sum T of all such terms is the kinetic energy of the system. The energy theorem then states that the sum of the kinetic and potential energies of the system is constant in time.

Symbolically

$$T + U = E, \quad \text{for all } t,$$

where E denotes the constant total energy.

5. We have derived four laws of conservation in all, namely those for

   (i) the total momentum,

   (ii) the expression $\sum_i m_i(\boldsymbol{r}_i - \dot{\boldsymbol{r}}_i t)$,

   (iii) the total angular momentum, and

   (iv) the total energy.

The theorem concerning the centroid follows at once from the first and second conservation laws. The first three laws are expressed by vectorial equations, and the fourth by a scalar equation. We therefore have $3 + 3 + 3 + 1 = 10$ functions of the coordinates and velocity components which remain constant in time when the independent variables in them are replaced by the corresponding solutions of the equations of motion.

We shall now turn to the theory of ordinary differential equations in so far as it is required. It will cast some new light on the conservation laws.

2. Ordinary differential equations

1. Let us introduce the velocity components u_i, v_i and w_i. Then Newton's equations of motion may be put into the form

$$\left. \begin{aligned} m_i \dot{u}_i &= X_i(u_1, v_1, \ldots \quad \ldots, y_n, z_n, t), \quad \text{etc.} \\ \dot{x}_i &= u_i, \quad \text{etc.} \end{aligned} \right\}$$

We have here supposed that the components of the forces are known functions of the coordinates, velocity components and of the time. The mechanical problem is now to find functions

$$\left. \begin{aligned} x_i &= \phi_i(t), & u_i &= \dot{\phi}_i(t) \\ y_i &= \psi_i(t), & v_i &= \dot{\psi}_i(t) \\ z_i &= \chi_i(t), & w_i &= \dot{\chi}_i(t) \end{aligned} \right\},$$

which satisfy Newton's equations identically, i.e. for all values of t. This is a special case of the central problem in the theory of ordinary differential equations, namely to find all solutions of the system of differential equations

$$\dot{x}_i = f_i(x_1, \ldots, x_m, t), \qquad i = 1, 2, \ldots, m,$$

i.e. all those functions

$$x_i = \phi_i(t), \qquad i = 1, 2, \ldots, m,$$

which make the system into an identity when we replace all the x_i by $\phi_i(t)$.

For the sake of simplicity we shall, in what follows, write x instead of $(x_1, x_2, \ldots, x_m)$ and the system of equations becomes

$$\dot{x}_i = f_i(x, t), \qquad i = 1, 2, \ldots, m.$$

We assume that the functions f_i are bounded functions of the $(m+1)$-dimensional vector (x, t) in the whole of $(m+1)$-dimensional vector space R^{m+1}. Further, they are assumed to be differentiable with respect to $x_1, x_2, \ldots, x_m$ for all (x, t), and the partial derivatives $\partial f_i / \partial x_j$ are everywhere continuous and uniformly bounded. These conditions are stricter, in fact, than purely mathematical considerations demand. For the purposes of mechanics, however, they are quite general enough, and they permit a particularly simple formulation of the main theorems enumerated below. The theorems are summarized again in Section 5, where the reader may, if he wishes, make himself acquainted with them without having to read the rest of the text.

The first, and most important, theorem concerns existence and uniqueness. It states that for every point $\overset{\circ}{x} = (\overset{\circ}{x}_1, \overset{\circ}{x}_2, \ldots, \overset{\circ}{x}_m)$ of m-dimensional number-space R^m and for every instant $\overset{\circ}{t}$ of time there is one and only one solution

$$x_i = \phi_i(\overset{\circ}{x}, \overset{\circ}{t}, t), \qquad i = 1, 2, \ldots, m,$$

of the system of differential equations

$$\dot{x}_i = f_i(x, t), \qquad i = 1, 2, \ldots, m,$$

which is defined for all t, and is such that

$$\overset{\circ}{x}_i = \phi_i(\overset{\circ}{x}, \overset{\circ}{t}, \overset{\circ}{t}).$$

(The functions ϕ_i are, of course, continuously differentiable with respect to t.)

To prove this we rewrite the differential equations as integral equations, by integrating with respect to the time variable t:

$$\phi_i(\overset{\circ}{x}, \overset{\circ}{t}, t) = \overset{\circ}{x}_i + \int_{\overset{\circ}{t}}^{t} f_i\{\phi(\overset{\circ}{x}, \overset{\circ}{t}, \tau), \tau\} \, \mathrm{d}\tau.$$

We prove that this system of integral equations does, in fact, possess a solution by constructing it in successive approximations. For this purpose we begin with any approximate solution $\phi_i^{(1)}(\overset{\circ}{x}, \overset{\circ}{t}, t)$, for example with

$$\phi_i^{(1)}(\overset{\circ}{x}, \overset{\circ}{t}, t) \equiv \overset{\circ}{x}_i,$$

and then construct second and third approximate solutions $\phi_i^{(2)}, \phi_i^{(3)}$, and so on, following the prescription

$$\phi_i^{(r+1)}(\overset{\circ}{x}, \overset{\circ}{t}, t) = \overset{\circ}{x}_i + \int_{\overset{\circ}{t}}^{t} f_i\{\phi^{(r)}(\overset{\circ}{x}, \overset{\circ}{t}, \tau), \tau\} \, \mathrm{d}\tau.$$

It may now be shown, successively,

(a) that the sequences $\{\phi_i^{(r)}\}$ converge uniformly to m continuous limit functions $\phi_i^*(\overset{\circ}{x}, \overset{\circ}{t}, t)$ in every bounded interval of time;

(b) that these limit functions satisfy the system of integral equations and therefore that of the differential equations;

(c) that they give the unique solutions for a given $\overset{\circ}{t}$ and $\overset{\circ}{x}$.

We refer to the literature for details of the steps in the proof.

We may add that the method of successive approximations also permits the numerical construction of a solution to any desired accuracy, as well as the improvement of any known approximate solution. It is possible in every case to make an exact estimate of the errors involved.

Finally, we shall state another two important theorems without giving a proof. The first states that the solution functions $\phi_i(\overset{\circ}{x}, \overset{\circ}{t}, t)$ are continuously differentiable with respect to the $(m+2)$ variables $\overset{\circ}{x}_1, ..., \overset{\circ}{x}_m, \overset{\circ}{t}, t$. The second theorem states that the solution functions ϕ_i are continuous with respect to the right-hand sides f_i of the system of differential equations in the following sense: When the right-hand sides of two systems of equations differ sufficiently little, then the corresponding solution functions differ by an arbitrarily small amount in every bounded interval of time.

We may picture these fundamental ideas in the following way. The system

$$\dot{x}_i = f_i(x, t)$$

of differential equations defines a velocity vector $\dot{x}$ for every point x of m-dimensional number space R^m and for every instant t; in other words it defines a velocity field. We may picture R^m filled by a continuously distributed substance whose motion is described by the velocity field, and we may then speak of a field of flow. The solution functions

$$x_i = \phi_i(\overset{0}{x}, \overset{0}{t}, t)$$

give a parametric representation of the one and only streamline through a given origin $\overset{0}{x}$ at an initial time $\overset{0}{t}$. If we let $\overset{0}{x}$ vary in the whole of R^m we obtain a second representation of the field of flow. While the former representation tells us what happens at every point x at any arbitrary instant t, the latter connects together two arbitrarily distant instants of time $\overset{0}{t}$ and t by stating into which x the point $\overset{0}{x}$ is carried during the time interval $\overset{0}{t}, \dots, t$.

2. We now invert this last idea by seeking the initial point $\overset{0}{x}$ at time $\overset{0}{t}$ which has gone over, at time $\overset{1}{t}$, into the point $\overset{1}{x}$. The appropriate streamline has the representation

$$x_i = \phi_i(\overset{0}{x}, \overset{0}{t}, t),$$

or, if $\overset{1}{x}$ is chosen as the initial point,

$$x_i = \phi_i(\overset{1}{x}, \overset{1}{t}, t).$$

It follows that

$$\overset{1}{x}_i = \phi_i(\overset{0}{x}, \overset{0}{t}, \overset{1}{t}),$$

and in the second representation

$$\overset{0}{x}_i = \phi_i(\overset{1}{x}, \overset{1}{t}, \overset{0}{t});$$

the latter is valid for every instant $\overset{1}{t}$ and the corresponding point $\overset{1}{x}$ on the streamline considered. We omit the superscript 1 and state: If the independent variables x_i in the functions $\phi_i(x, t, \overset{0}{t})$ are replaced by the functions $\phi_i(\overset{0}{x}, \overset{0}{t}, t)$ then the corresponding coordinate of the initial point is obtained. Symbolically

$$\phi_i\{\phi(\overset{0}{x}, \overset{0}{t}, t), t, \overset{0}{t}\} = \overset{0}{x}_i, \qquad i = 1, \dots, m,$$

for all $\overset{0}{x}$, $\overset{0}{t}$ and t. Briefly, then, if the image point $x = \phi(\overset{0}{x}, \overset{0}{t}, t)$ belongs, at time t, to the initial point $\overset{0}{x}$, then, conversely, the initial point $\overset{0}{x} = \phi(x, t, \overset{0}{t})$ belongs to this image point.

Suppose that a non-constant function $\psi(x, t)$ of the independent variables x, t is constant "along each streamline", i.e. that the value of the function $\psi\{\phi(\overset{0}{x}, \overset{0}{t}, t), t, \overset{0}{t}\}$ is equal, for all t, to its initial value for $t = \overset{0}{t}$. Then we call ψ a first integral (or, for short, an integral) of the system of differential equations. This implies that

$$\psi\{\phi(\overset{0}{x}, \overset{0}{t}, t), t\} = \psi(\overset{0}{x}, \overset{0}{t})$$

for all $\overset{0}{x}$, $\overset{0}{t}$ and t. But, by definition,

$$\phi_i(\overset{0}{x}, \overset{0}{t}, \overset{0}{t}) = \overset{0}{x}_i, \qquad i = 1, 2, ..., m.$$

The equation defining the concept of a first integral is therefore

$$\psi\{\phi(\overset{0}{x}, \overset{0}{t}, t), t\} = \psi(\overset{0}{x}, \overset{0}{t}),$$

for all $\overset{0}{x}$, $\overset{0}{t}$ and t.

We see that the m functions $\phi_i(x, t, \overset{0}{t})$ are integrals. ($\overset{0}{t}$ is to be regarded as a fixed parameter in all these considerations; we retain it to bring out clearly the duality between the initial point and the moving point.)

We now ask how many first integrals there are. The immediate answer is that there are an infinite number. Evidently any arbitrary (non-constant) function of one or several integrals remains constant along every streamline and is therefore itself an integral. The question must be made more precise and we therefore ask how many *independent* integrals there are.

We recall that the r functions $g_1(x, t), g_2(x, t), ..., g_r(x, t)$ are said to be mutually dependent when there exists a non-constant function $G(u_1, u_2, ..., u_r)$ of the r independent variables $u_1, u_2, ..., u_r$ such that

$$G\{g_1(x, t), g_2(x, t), ..., g_r(x, t)\} = 0,$$

for all x and t. If there is no such function G one says that the functions $g_1, g_2, ..., g_r$ are mutually independent.

We now state, first of all, that the m integrals $\phi_i(x, t, \overset{0}{t})$ are mutually independent, so that there are, in any case, at least m independent integrals.

If, in fact, there existed a non-constant function $G(u_1, u_2, ..., u_m)$, such that the equation

$$G\{\phi_1(x, t, \overset{\scriptscriptstyle 0}{t}),\ \phi_2(x, t, \overset{\scriptscriptstyle 0}{t}),\ ...,\ \phi_m(x, t, \overset{\scriptscriptstyle 0}{t})\} = 0$$

were satisfied for all x and t, then it would follow, in particular, for $t = \overset{\scriptscriptstyle 0}{t}$, that

$$G(x_1, x_2, ..., x_m) = 0$$

for all vectors x—contrary to the condition that G is non-constant.

We then state, in the second place, that there are not more than m independent integrals. In proof of this we show, first, that for any arbitrary integral ψ there can be chosen a non-constant function $G(u_1, ..., u_{m+1})$ of the $(m+1)$ independent variables $u_1, ..., u_{m+1}$, which is such that $G(\phi_1, ..., \phi_m, \psi) = 0$ for all x and t. For let

$$x_i = \phi_i(\overset{\scriptscriptstyle 1}{x}, \overset{\scriptscriptstyle 1}{t}, t)$$

represent the streamline through the fixed point $(\overset{\scriptscriptstyle 1}{x}, \overset{\scriptscriptstyle 1}{t})$. Its origin at time $\overset{\scriptscriptstyle 0}{t}$ is

$$\overset{\scriptscriptstyle 0}{x}_i = \phi_i(\overset{\scriptscriptstyle 1}{x}, \overset{\scriptscriptstyle 1}{t}, \overset{\scriptscriptstyle 0}{t}).$$

But $\psi(x, t)$ is an integral, so that

$$\psi(\overset{\scriptscriptstyle 1}{x}, \overset{\scriptscriptstyle 1}{t}) = \psi(\overset{\scriptscriptstyle 0}{x}, \overset{\scriptscriptstyle 0}{t})$$
$$= \psi\{\phi(\overset{\scriptscriptstyle 1}{x}, \overset{\scriptscriptstyle 1}{t}, \overset{\scriptscriptstyle 0}{t}), \overset{\scriptscriptstyle 0}{t}\},$$

for every point $(\overset{\scriptscriptstyle 1}{x}, \overset{\scriptscriptstyle 1}{t})$ in space-time. Thus

$$\psi(x, t) = \psi\{\phi(x, t, \overset{\scriptscriptstyle 0}{t}), \overset{\scriptscriptstyle 0}{t}\}$$

for all (x, t). If we put

$$u_{m+1} - \psi(u_1, ..., u_m, \overset{\scriptscriptstyle 0}{t}) \equiv G(u_1, ..., u_{m+1}),$$

then G is certainly a non-constant function of the $(m+1)$ independent variables $u_1, ..., u_{m+1}$ and

$$G(\phi_1, ..., \phi_m, \psi) = 0$$

is satisfied. The $(m+1)$ integrals $\phi_1, ..., \phi_m, \psi$ are therefore mutually dependent.

The fact that any $(m+1)$ integrals $\psi_1(x, t), ..., \psi_{m+1}(x, t)$ are mutually dependent can be made plausible in the following way. We express each integral as a function of the particular integrals ϕ_i

$$\psi_\alpha(x, t) = \psi_\alpha(\overset{\scriptscriptstyle 0}{x}, \overset{\scriptscriptstyle 0}{t})$$
$$= \psi_\alpha\{\phi(x, t, \overset{\scriptscriptstyle 0}{t}), \overset{\scriptscriptstyle 0}{t}\}, \qquad \alpha = 1, 2, ..., m,$$

r all (x, t). If we can, with a suitable numbering of the func-
ons ψ_α, use the first m of these equations to find the integrals ϕ_i
functions of the integrals $\psi_1, \ldots, \psi_m$, then we shall enter with
ese expressions into the $(m+1)^{\text{th}}$ equation and obtain an
pression for ψ_{m+1} as a function of the other ψ_i. The integrals
, $\ldots, \psi_{m+1}$ are then mutually dependent. If the m equations
nnot be solved for ϕ_i, then the determinant of the matrix
$\|\partial\psi_i/\partial x_j\|$ must vanish. In this case, according to a well-known
eorem about functional determinants, the functions $\psi_1, \ldots, \psi_m$
e mutually dependent, and so, *a fortiori*, are the functions
, $\ldots, \psi_{m+1}$. For the theorems about these determinants we refer
ae reader to the literature.

To summarize what we shall need: There is a maximum number
of independent integrals of the system of differential equations

$$\dot{x}_i = f_i(x, t), \qquad i = 1, \ldots, m;$$

nversely, there is a set of at least m independent integrals and
ese are the m functions $\phi_1(x, t, \overset{\circ}{t}), \ldots, \phi_m(x, t, \overset{\circ}{t})$ which are derived
om the solution functions by the interchange of (x, t) and $(\overset{\circ}{x}, \overset{\circ}{t})$.
We have tacitly taken the functions ψ_i to be differentiable.
a what follows we shall consider, whenever necessary, that such
rmal mathematical conditions are fulfilled without explicitly
ating this in every case.

3. We have now explained the concept of a (first) integral as
llows: The function $\psi(x, t)$ is called an integral of the system of
fferential equations if, and only if,

$$\psi\{\phi(\overset{\circ}{x}, \overset{\circ}{t}, t), t\} = \psi(\overset{\circ}{x}, \overset{\circ}{t}),$$

r all $\overset{\circ}{x}$, $\overset{\circ}{t}$ and t. It is sometimes useful to present this equation
the differential form, which is obtained on differentiating with
spect to the time t. We introduce the abbreviations

$$\dot{\psi}(x, t) \equiv \frac{\partial}{\partial t}\psi(x, t), \quad \psi_j(x, t) \equiv \frac{\partial}{\partial x_j}\psi(x, t),$$

$$\dot{\phi}_j(\overset{\circ}{x}, \overset{\circ}{t}, t) \equiv \frac{\partial}{\partial t}\phi_j(\overset{\circ}{x}, \overset{\circ}{t}, t),$$

and obtain the equation

$$\psi\{\phi(\mathring{x},\mathring{t},t),t\} + \sum_{j=1}^{m}\psi_j\{\phi(\mathring{x},\mathring{t},t),t\}\cdot\phi_j(\mathring{x},\mathring{t},t) = 0,$$

for all $\mathring{x}$, $\mathring{t}$ and t. The system of differential equations is

$$\dot{x}_i = f_i(x,t),$$

i.e. $$\dot{\phi}_i(x_0,t_0,t) = f_i\{\phi(\mathring{x},\mathring{t},t),t\},$$

and so the above equation may be written

$$\dot{\psi}\{\phi(\mathring{x},\mathring{t},t),t\} + \sum_{j=1}^{m}\psi_j\{\phi(\mathring{x},\mathring{t},t),t\}\cdot f_j\{\phi(\mathring{x},\mathring{t},t),t\} = 0,$$

for all $\mathring{x},\mathring{t},t$.

We may therefore write

$$\dot{\psi}(x,t) + \sum_{j=1}^{m}\psi_j(x,t)f_j(x,t) = 0,$$

for all x and t, where the x_i are now *independent* variables. Th transition from the functions $\phi_i(\mathring{x},\mathring{t},t)$ to the independent variable x_i is permissible. For, with a given $\mathring{t}$ and t, it is possible t find an $\mathring{x}$, corresponding to an arbitrarily chosen x, such tha $x = \phi(\mathring{x},\mathring{t},t)$, and the last equation but one is valid for all The last equation therefore also holds for all x.

This linear partial differential equation

$$\frac{\partial\psi}{\partial t} + \sum_{j=1}^{m}\frac{\partial\psi}{\partial x_j}f_j(x,t) = 0$$

does not involve the solution functions $\phi_i(\mathring{x},\mathring{t},t)$, which are fre quently unknown in any case. It is called the Liouville equatio of the system of differential equations

$$\dot{x}_i = f_i(x,t);$$

conversely, one calls this the characteristic system of the partia differential equation. We have thus shown that if $\psi(x,t)$ is a integral of the system of differential equations, then $\psi(x,t)$ sati fies the corresponding Liouville equation.

The following converse is also true. If a function $\psi(x,t)$ satisfie a partial differential equation of Liouville's type then it is a integral of the corresponding characteristic system. To prove this, one only needs to reverse the reasoning leading to Liouville's equation.

We now apply to the Liouville equation our results about the multiplicity of first integrals and find, immediately: Given m functions $f_i(x, t)$, the linear partial differential equation

$$\frac{\partial \psi}{\partial t} + \sum_{j=1}^{m} f_j(x, t) \frac{\partial \psi}{\partial x_j} = 0$$

has exactly m independent solutions $\psi(x, t)$. Suppose, further, that $\psi(x, t)$ coincides with any arbitrary function $\overset{\circ}{\psi}(x)$ for $t = \overset{\circ}{t}$. Then the differential equation and the initial conditions are satisfied by the function

$$\psi(x, t) \equiv \overset{\circ}{\psi}\{\phi(x, t, \overset{\circ}{t})\},$$

where the functions $\phi_i(x, t, \overset{\circ}{t})$ denote the particular integrals of the system of characteristic equations. This is evidently the only function $\psi(x, t)$ which does so.

4. We were led to the concept of the first integral by inverting, in a sense, the concept of a solution function of the system of differential equations

$$\dot{x}_i = f_i(x, t), \qquad i = 1, \dots, m.$$

The knowledge of one such integral of the system enables us to reduce by one the order of the system. For the equation

$$\psi(x, t) = C,$$

with C a suitable arbitrary constant, states that the streamline

$$x_i = \phi_i(\overset{\circ}{x}, \overset{\circ}{t}, t)$$

must lie on a certain $(m - 1)$-dimensional hypersurface which is moving through the m-dimensional space R^m. The problem is thus reduced to $(m - 1)$ dimensions. Analytically one may, for example, solve the equation $\psi = C$ for x_m, if this is possible, and obtain

$$x_m = \text{function of } (x_1, \dots, x_{m-1}, t, C).$$

This is substituted into the system of differential equations, of which the final equation may then be disregarded. In practice, of course, one has to remember that the function x_m is only determined uniquely "in the small".

Similarly, when k integrals are known ($k \leqslant m$), the system may be reduced to $(m-k)$ equations. If $k = m$ the problem is solved except for the construction of the inverse functions to give the moving point x as a function of the time and of the m arbitrary constants $C_1, ..., C_m$. Finally these constants of integration have to be expressed in terms of the coordinates of the initial point $\overset{\circ}{x}$. From

$$C_i = \psi_i(x, t)$$

it follows that

$$C_i = \psi_i(\overset{\circ}{x}, \overset{\circ}{t}).$$

In the previous section we discussed the conservation laws of mechanics, namely the laws of conservation of energy, of momentum, of the expression $\sum_i m_i(\boldsymbol{r}_i - t\dot{\boldsymbol{r}}_i)$ and of angular momentum. These laws give $1 + (3 \times 3) = 10$ integrals, and make it possible, in principle, to reduce by 10 the order of the system of equations of motion. But difficulties may occur in particular cases, especially when the energy integral is used, in representing the inverse functions by means of formulae. If so, one can only make a reduction of smaller order.

5. We now summarize the principal results of this paragraph:

(a) The existence and uniqueness theorems hold for the solutions $\phi_i(\overset{\circ}{x}, \overset{\circ}{t}, t)$ of the system of differential equations

$$\dot{x}_i = f_i(x, t), \qquad i = 1, 2, ..., m.$$

The solution functions $\phi_i(\overset{\circ}{x}, \overset{\circ}{t}, t)$ are continuously differentiable with respect to all their arguments. They depend continuously on the right-hand sides $f_i(x, t)$ of the system of differential equations.

(b) Their inverse functions, with respect to the coordinates, are the functions $\phi_i(x, t, \overset{\circ}{t})$.

(c) These are (first) integrals of the system. We call a non-constant function $\psi(x, t)$ a (first) integral if it is constant along each streamline.

(d) There is an infinity of sets of m independent first integrals. The members of any group of $(m+1)$ integrals are mutually dependent.

(e) The (first) integrals satisfy the Liouville equation, and every solution of the Liouville equation is a first integral.

(f) The Liouville equation has exactly m independent solutions, in the absence of constraints of any kind, and has one and only one solution for a given initial condition.

(g) Every known integral can be used to reduce by one the order of the system of differential equations.

5. Poincaré's recurrence theorem

1. In a theory of a stellar or of any mechanical system, as formulated in II.4, the first basic problem is the calculation of its evolution. The theory of differential equations shows directly how this may be done, at least in principle. One has to deduce, from the appropriate equations of motion, both the positions and the velocities of the particles as functions of the time, of the initial positions and of the initial velocities. In a particular case, however, one can do so only approximately and for limited intervals of time, if it can be done at all. But this way does not in general lead to a *description* of the evolution of the mechanical system *in the large*. Poincaré's recurrence theorem is useful here, under certain conditions. We formulate it in this way:

Let the right-hand sides of the system of differential equations

$$\dot{x}_i = f_i(x), \qquad i = 1, 2, ..., m$$

be independent of time, and let them satisfy the condition

$$\sum_{j=1}^{m} \frac{\partial}{\partial x_j} f_j(x) \equiv 0.$$

Further let there be, in the space R^m of the m-tuple numbers $x = (x_1, x_2, ..., x_m)$, a set of points J with a positive finite (hyper-)volume (or positive finite Lebesgue measure) equal to $m(J)$. Let this set be such that the streamline

$$x_i = \phi_i(\overset{\circ}{x}, t)$$

lies entirely in J for every initial point $\overset{\circ}{x} \in J$ at time $t = 0$. Then "almost every" initial point $\overset{\circ}{x} \in J$ is a point of accumulation of the corresponding sequence of points

$$\phi(\overset{\circ}{x}, \tau), \; \phi(\overset{\circ}{x}, 2\tau), \; \phi(\overset{\circ}{x}, 3\tau), \; \ldots$$

and of the sequence

$$\phi(\overset{\circ}{x}, -\tau), \; \phi(\overset{\circ}{x}, -2\tau), \; \phi(\overset{\circ}{x}, -3\tau), \; \ldots,$$

where τ is an arbitrary positive constant. The constants $\overset{\circ}{l}$ in the solution functions ϕ_i have been put equal to zero above and will be put equal to zero below, and they are omitted altogether from now on.

Every subset M of R^m will be called an invariant subset of R^m if it has the property that the flow ϕ transforms it into itself at all times. This invariance is expressed symbolically by

$$\phi(M, t) = M, \quad \text{for all } t.$$

The invariant region J is assumed to have positive finite measure. We think here of Lebesgue measure, which is used only to ensure the *existence* of a content for the sets considered. Readers who are unfamiliar with the ideas of Lebesgue theory may use instead the ordinary (Riemannian) ideas. But they must always add to the text the proviso "in so far as the content exists", and to assume, by hypothesis, its existence. In the formulation of the theorem, the expression "almost every point" means that the set A of exceptional points $\overset{\circ}{x}$, which do not satisfy the theorem, has zero Lebesgue measure.

The recurrence theorem states, to put it rather unrigorously, that the moving point approaches, on every streamline in J, arbitrarily close to its initial point again and again, under the given conditions. This is valid for both directions in time. Now any point on a streamline may be considered to be an initial point. Thus the moving point comes back arbitrarily closely to every point on the streamline again and again.

The recurrence theorem shows that the evolution of a mechanical system is quasi-periodic, as we might say, provided certain conditions are fulfilled. The quasi-periodicity does not apply to all lines of evolution, but the exceptional cases without this property are in a vanishingly small minority. One need not reckon with the possibility of meeting such a case in practice.

2. Consider a system of particles with the equations of motion

$$
\left.
\begin{aligned}
m_i \dot{u}_i &= X_i(x_1, \ldots, x_n, y_1, \ldots, y_n, z_1, \ldots, z_n), \\
m_i \dot{v}_i &= Y_i(x_1, \ldots, z_n), \\
m_i \dot{w}_i &= Z_i(x_1, \ldots, z_n), \\
\dot{x}_i &= u_i, \\
\dot{y}_i &= v_i, \\
\dot{z}_i &= w_i,
\end{aligned}
\right\}
$$

where $i = 1, \ldots, n$. The right-hand sides of these equations are evidently time-independent and the expression $\sum_1^m (\partial f_j / \partial x_j)$ vanishes, i.e.

$$
\sum_{j=1}^n \frac{\partial X_j}{\partial u_j} + \frac{\partial Y_j}{\partial v_j} + \frac{\partial Z_j}{\partial w_j} + \frac{\partial u_j}{\partial x_j} + \frac{\partial v_j}{\partial y_j} + \frac{\partial w_j}{\partial z_j} \equiv 0.
$$

The known time-independent integrals of the equations of motion enable us to define invariant regions in R^{6n} with the coordinates $u_1, \ldots, u_n, \ v_1, \ldots, v_n, \ w_1, \ldots, w_n, \ x_1, \ldots, x_n, \ y_1, \ldots, y_n, \ z_1, \ldots, z_n$. If ψ is such an integral and α, β are two suitably chosen constants, with $\alpha < \beta$, then, for instance, the set of all points of R^{6n} satisfying $\alpha < \psi < \beta$ is an invariant region of this type.

We shall now try to find such a region with a finite positive measure. For this purpose we require an integral for which the surfaces $\psi = \text{const.}$ do not all extend to infinity. We require, in particular, the energy integral which will, once again, be denoted by H. We assume that the forces are negative gradients of a time-independent potential $U(\mathbf{r}_1, \ldots, \mathbf{r}_n)$ and have that

$$
H = \tfrac{1}{2} \sum_1^n m_j (u_j^2 + v_j^2 + w_j^2) + U(\mathbf{r}_1, \ldots, \mathbf{r}_n),
$$

while the invariant region J is the set of all points of R^{6n} for which

$$
\alpha < H < \beta.
$$

The particular nature of the potential U determines whether it is, in fact, possible to find constants α and β such that

$$
0 < m(J) < \infty.
$$

D

If the function H attains an extremum, say a minimum, in the strict sense at any point P of R^{6n}, then there can always be defined an invariant region J with a finite positive $m(J)$. One can, without any loss of generality, assume this minimum value to be zero, since the equations of motion are unchanged when an arbitrary constant is added to U, or, consequently, to H. To construct the region we describe a small $6n$-dimensional sphere K about P, the minimum point. The function H attains a minimum value h on the surface of K, and h is positive provided only that K has been chosen sufficiently small. The intersection, D, of K with the set M of all the points in R^{6n} which satisfy the condition $H < h$ is then an invariant region of finite positive measure. The invariance of D follows in this way: No image point of a point in D can lie outside K. If this were possible the flow would have to cross the boundary of K, where the value of H would have to be not less than h. On the other hand H is a first integral and must retain its initial values, which are all smaller than h, according to our definition of D. It follows that the part of M lying inside K is invariant, as stated. We evidently have $m(D) \leqslant m(K) < \infty$. Further, $m(D) > 0$, because the boundary points of D have a certain positive minimum distance from P so that there exists a sphere surrounding P lying entirely within D.

If U has no lower bound the region J between the energy surfaces $H = \alpha$ and $H = \beta$ extends to infinity and has infinite measure, in general.

The other integrals of the equations of motion can be used as well for the definition of boundaries of invariant regions. But the level surfaces belonging to them all extend to infinity, so that one still needs the energy integral in every case.

3. For the proof of the recurrence theorem we require the following lemma, named after Liouville.

Let the system of differential equations

$$\dot{x}_i = f_i(x, t), \qquad i = 1, \ldots, m,$$

have the general solution $x_i = \phi_i(\overset{\circ}{x}, t)$, where $\overset{\circ}{x}_i = \phi_i(\overset{\circ}{x}, 0)$. Further, let $\Delta = \Delta(\overset{\circ}{x}, t)$ be the determinant of the matrix

$$\left\| \frac{\partial}{\partial \overset{\circ}{x}_j} \phi_i(\overset{\circ}{x}, t) \right\|.$$

en

$$\frac{\partial \Delta}{\partial t} = \Delta \sum_{j=1}^{m} \left\{ \frac{\partial}{\partial x_j} f_j(x,t) \right\}_{x=\phi(\overset{\circ}{x},t)},$$

ere we substitute $\phi_i(\overset{\circ}{x},t)$ for x_i on the right-hand side after fferentiation. It may be emphasized that the right-hand sides f_i ay depend explicitly on the time t.

For the sake of simplicity in writing we shall confine our proof the case $m = 2$, when

$$\Delta = \begin{vmatrix} \dfrac{\partial \phi_1}{\partial \overset{\circ}{x}_1} & \dfrac{\partial \phi_1}{\partial \overset{\circ}{x}_2} \\[2mm] \dfrac{\partial \phi_2}{\partial \overset{\circ}{x}_1} & \dfrac{\partial \phi_2}{\partial \overset{\circ}{x}_2} \end{vmatrix}.$$

ifferentiation with respect to the time yields

$$\frac{\partial \Delta}{\partial t} = \begin{vmatrix} \dfrac{\partial^2 \phi_1}{\partial t\, \partial \overset{\circ}{x}_1} & \dfrac{\partial^2 \phi_1}{\partial t\, \partial \overset{\circ}{x}_2} \\[2mm] \dfrac{\partial \phi_2}{\partial \overset{\circ}{x}_1} & \dfrac{\partial \phi_2}{\partial \overset{\circ}{x}_2} \end{vmatrix} + \begin{vmatrix} \dfrac{\partial \phi_1}{\partial \overset{\circ}{x}_1} & \dfrac{\partial \phi_1}{\partial \overset{\circ}{x}_2} \\[2mm] \dfrac{\partial^2 \phi_2}{\partial t\, \partial \overset{\circ}{x}_1} & \dfrac{\partial^2 \phi_2}{\partial t\, \partial \overset{\circ}{x}_2} \end{vmatrix}.$$

place of

$$\frac{\partial^2 \phi_1}{\partial t\, \partial \overset{\circ}{x}_1} \equiv \frac{\partial}{\partial \overset{\circ}{x}_1} \frac{\partial \phi_1}{\partial t}$$

now write

$$\frac{\partial}{\partial \overset{\circ}{x}_1} f_1(x,t),$$

d replace this by

$$\sum_{j=1}^{2} \frac{\partial f_1}{\partial x_j} \frac{\partial \phi_j}{\partial \overset{\circ}{x}_1}.$$

hen the other elements have been transformed in the same ay the first determinant in the expression for $\partial \Delta / \partial t$ becomes

$$\begin{vmatrix} \sum_j \dfrac{\partial f_1}{\partial x_j} \dfrac{\partial \phi_j}{\partial \overset{\circ}{x}_1} & \sum_j \dfrac{\partial f_1}{\partial x_j} \dfrac{\partial \phi_j}{\partial \overset{\circ}{x}_2} \\[2mm] \dfrac{\partial \phi_2}{\partial \overset{\circ}{x}_1} & \dfrac{\partial \phi_2}{\partial \overset{\circ}{x}_2} \end{vmatrix}$$

$$= \sum_{j=1}^{2} \frac{\partial f_1}{\partial x_j} \begin{vmatrix} \dfrac{\partial \phi_j}{\partial \overset{\circ}{x}_1} & \dfrac{\partial \phi_j}{\partial \overset{\circ}{x}_2} \\[2mm] \dfrac{\partial \phi_2}{\partial \overset{\circ}{x}_1} & \dfrac{\partial \phi_2}{\partial \overset{\circ}{x}_2} \end{vmatrix}$$

$$= \frac{\partial f_1}{\partial x_1} \Delta + \frac{\partial f_1}{\partial x_2} \times 0 \qquad = \frac{\partial f_1}{\partial x_1} \Delta.$$

It follows that
$$\frac{\partial \Delta}{\partial t} = \frac{\partial f_1}{\partial x_1} \Delta + \frac{\partial f_2}{\partial x_2} \Delta,$$

as stated above.

If, further,
$$\sum_{j=1}^{m} \frac{\partial f_j}{\partial x_j} \equiv 0,$$

then it follows from Liouville's theorem that the determinant

$$\Delta(\overset{\circ}{x}, t) = 1$$

for all $\overset{\circ}{x}$ and t.

For
$$\frac{\partial \Delta}{\partial t} = \Delta \sum_{1}^{m} \frac{\partial f_j}{\partial x_j}$$

vanishes, by hypothesis. But, when $t = 0$,

$$\left\{ \frac{\partial}{\partial \overset{\circ}{x}_j} \phi_i(\overset{\circ}{x}, t) \right\}_{t=0} = \frac{\partial \overset{\circ}{x}_i}{\partial \overset{\circ}{x}_j} = \delta_{ij} = \begin{cases} 1, \text{ when } i = j \\ 0, \text{ when } i \neq j, \end{cases}$$

for all $\overset{\circ}{x}$. It follows that, for all t and $\overset{\circ}{x}$,

$$\Delta(\overset{\circ}{x}, t) = \Delta(\overset{\circ}{x}, 0) = \det \| \delta_{ij} \| = 1.$$

Conversely, it follows from $\Delta(\overset{\circ}{x}, t) \equiv 1$ that

$$\sum_{1}^{m} \frac{\partial f_j}{\partial x_j} \equiv 0.$$

This stricter form of Liouville's theorem holds for a mechanic system in which the forces are independent of the velocity com ponents (following the explanation at the beginning of Section 2 In our formulation it applies to Cartesian coordinates and th corresponding velocity components. In the case of gener coordinates the theorem remains true only if the appropria momenta are substituted for the rates of change of the coordi ates. In the mechanics of stellar systems the more gener formulation is not often used, and so we shall not give it here.

4. The functional determinant $\Delta(\overset{\circ}{x}, t)$ arises in this way.

Let $\overset{\circ}{G}$ be any region of initial points $\overset{\circ}{x}$ in "phase-space" R^m (a we shall call it from now on). Let the image points $x = \phi(\overset{\circ}{x},$ correspond to these initial points $\overset{\circ}{x}$, at time t. Now the mappir $x = \phi(\overset{\circ}{x}, t)$ of the space R^m into itself is continuous and one-to-or for all t. Therefore the points $\phi(\overset{\circ}{x}, t)$ form a region with a measure $m(G)$ given by

$$m(G) = \int_G \cdots \int dx_1, \ldots, \quad dx_n$$

or, in abbreviation, $m(G) = \int_G dx.$

By the rule for the transformation of volume integrals

$$\int_G dx = \int_{\overset{\circ}{G}} \det \left\| \frac{\partial}{\partial \overset{\circ}{x}_j} \phi_i(\overset{\circ}{x}, t) \right\| d\overset{\circ}{x} = \int_{\overset{\circ}{G}} \Delta(\overset{\circ}{x}, t) \, d\overset{\circ}{x}.$$

This is where one meets the determinant $\Delta(\overset{\circ}{x}, t)$.

It follows from the restricted Liouville theorem

$$\Delta(\overset{\circ}{x}, t) \equiv 1$$

that the image region G and the initial region $\overset{\circ}{G}$ have equal measures

$$m(G) = m(\overset{\circ}{G}),$$

so that the measure is invariant with respect to the flow ϕ. We may say that the flow is metrically invariant.

Conversely, the metrical invariance of the flow ϕ implies that

$$\Delta(\overset{\circ}{x}, t) \equiv 1$$

everywhere and at all times. For from

$$\int_G dx - \int_{\overset{\circ}{G}} d\overset{\circ}{x} = 0$$

it follows that $\int_{\overset{\circ}{G}} \{\Delta(\overset{\circ}{x}, t) - 1\} \, d\overset{\circ}{x} = 0.$

Now the region $\overset{\circ}{G}$ can be chosen arbitrarily so that

$$\Delta(\overset{\circ}{x}, t) = 1$$

"almost everywhere". The function $\Delta(\overset{\circ}{x}, t)$ is continuous and must therefore equal unity everywhere.

Liouville's theorem, in its restricted sense, therefore shows that each of the three statements

$$\sum_j \frac{\partial}{\partial x_j} f_j(x, t) \equiv 0. \quad \Delta(\overset{\circ}{x}, t) \equiv 1, \quad \int_G dx = \int_{\overset{\circ}{G}} d\overset{\circ}{x}$$

implies the other two.

5. We now reformulate the recurrence theorem by means of the concept of a metrically invariant mapping.

For every t, let ϕ be a one-to-one, continuous and metrically invariant mapping of the m-dimensional space R^m into itself, let it vary continuously with the parameter t, and let it coincide with the identical mapping for $t = 0$. Further, let the following commutation law for successive transformations hold for all points $\overset{\circ}{x}$ and parameters t_1 and t_2, namely

$$\phi\{\phi(\overset{\circ}{x}, t_1), t_2\} = \phi(\overset{\circ}{x}, t_1 + t_2)$$
$$= \phi\{\phi(\overset{\circ}{x}, t_2), t_1\}.$$

Finally, let there be an "invariant subset" $J \subset R^m$ with a finite positive measure $m(J)$. We shall call a point $\overset{\circ}{x}$ of J a recurrence point with respect to the future if there is a positive constant τ such that $\overset{\circ}{x}$ is a point of accumulation of the sequence

$$\phi(\overset{\circ}{x}, \tau), \ \phi(\overset{\circ}{x}, 2\tau), \ \phi(\overset{\circ}{x}, 3\tau), \ \dots.$$

If $\overset{\circ}{x}$ is a point of accumulation of the sequence

$$\phi(\overset{\circ}{x}, -\tau), \ \phi(\overset{\circ}{x}, -2\tau), \ \phi(\overset{\circ}{x}, -3\tau), \ \dots$$

(possibly with a different τ) then $\overset{\circ}{x}$ is a recurrence point with respect to the past. The theorem states that "almost all" points $\overset{\circ}{x}$ of J are recurrence points with respect to both future and past for every arbitrarily chosen τ.

This formulation of the theorem does not refer to a system of differential equations, but to a certain group of transformations in R^m.

We now have to make certain that the solutions

$$x_i = \phi_i(\overset{\circ}{x}, t), \qquad i = 1, \dots, m$$

of the system of differential equations

$$\dot{x}_i = f_i(x)$$

with the initial values $\overset{\circ}{x}_i = \phi_i(\overset{\circ}{x}, 0)$, do in fact satisfy the stated conditions about the mapping ϕ. It is not possible to prove, nor is it true, that an invariant set J exists, with $0 < m(J) < \infty$, for any arbitrary set of functions $f_i(x)$. This must be assumed explicitly as an additional hypothesis. It only remains to demonstrate the validity of the commutation rule. The latter is an immediate consequence of the fact that the functions $f_i(x)$ are independent of the time variable t, and that therefore there is no change with time in the field of flow and in the streamlines. For if

$$\overset{1}{x} = \phi(\overset{0}{x}, \overset{1}{t})$$

and

$$\overset{2}{x} = \phi(\overset{1}{x}, \overset{2}{t}),$$

then

$$\overset{2}{x} = \phi(\overset{0}{x}, \overset{1}{t} + \overset{2}{t})$$

as stated. To show this analytically, we note that the set of differential equations

$$\dot{x}_i = f_i(x)$$

has the solution $$x_i = \phi_i(\overset{0}{x}, t - t_0)$$

for a particular initial time $\overset{0}{t}$. It is evident, on substitution, that these functions satisfy the equations if the functions $\phi_i(\overset{0}{x}, t)$ do so. They also satisfy the initial condition that they should equal $\overset{0}{x}_i$ for time $t = \overset{0}{t}$. Thus if

$$\overset{1}{x} = \phi(\overset{0}{x}, \overset{1}{t} - \overset{0}{t}),$$

then the streamline through $\overset{0}{x}$ may be described both by

$$x = \phi(\overset{0}{x}, t - \overset{0}{t})$$

and by $$x = \phi(\overset{1}{x}, t - \overset{1}{t}).$$

It follows that $$\phi(\overset{1}{x}, t - \overset{1}{t}) = \phi(\overset{0}{x}, t - \overset{0}{t})$$

or $$\phi\{\phi(\overset{0}{x}, \overset{1}{t} - \overset{0}{t}), t - \overset{1}{t}\} = \phi\{\overset{0}{x}, (\overset{1}{t} - \overset{0}{t}) + (t - \overset{1}{t})\},$$

which is another way of writing the original statement.

A flow like this with a time-independent velocity field is said to be stationary.

6. There is a simple way of picturing the basic idea behind the proof of the recurrence theorem. Consider any fixed subset $\overset{0}{M}$ of J with a positive measure $m(\overset{0}{M})$. Its image subset $M = \phi(\overset{0}{M}, t - \overset{0}{t})$ describes, in the course of time, a tube of flow, or, in other words, a bundle of streamlines whose volume would grow beyond all bounds, if the tube of flow never penetrated into itself again. But the content cannot grow indefinitely, for the tube of flow is a subset of J, and so cannot have a volume greater than that of J. On the other hand J has a finite volume. It follows that the tube of flow must

penetrate into itself somewhere, however thin it may be. But the flow ϕ is stationary so that no instant t and no "cross-section" of the tube of flow is preferred to any other. It follows that this self-penetration must occur at every place, and the recurrence occurs everywhere along the tube. This is true for all tubes of flow.

The proof itself sharpens this rather vaguely expressed basic idea. We divide it into the four steps (a) to (d), described below.

(a) Let $\overset{\circ}{M}$ be a fixed open (or closed) subset of J, and let τ be an arbitrary positive constant. Then there is, for every $\overset{\circ}{M}$ and every τ, a positive integer q such that the image $\phi(\overset{\circ}{M}, q\tau)$ of $\overset{\circ}{M}$ at time $q\tau$ has a non-empty intersection with the set $\overset{\circ}{M}$.

(b) Let δ be an arbitrary positive constant, and let A_δ be the set of all initial points $\overset{\circ}{x}$ in J, for which all points of the sequence

$$(\overset{\circ}{x}, +\tau),\ (\overset{\circ}{x}, -\tau),\ (\overset{\circ}{x}, +2\tau),\ (\overset{\circ}{x}, -2\tau),\ \ldots$$

have a distance greater than δ from $\overset{\circ}{x}$. Then the set A_δ is measurable.

(c) The set A_δ has measure zero.

(d) The set A of all non-recurrence points in J has the measure zero.

The statement (d) is the recurrence theorem.

7. We first prove the statement (a), that a positive integer q can be found, for every open or closed subset $\overset{\circ}{M}$ of J and for every positive constant τ, such that the sets $\overset{\circ}{M}$ and $\phi(\overset{\circ}{M}, q\tau)$ have a non-zero intersection.

For suppose that $\overset{\circ}{M}$ and $\phi(\overset{\circ}{M}, \tau)$ have no common point; if they have a common point nothing remains to be proved. Now the mapping is one-to-one in both directions, therefore the sets $\phi(\overset{\circ}{M}, \tau)$ and $\phi\{\phi(\overset{\circ}{M}, \tau), \tau\} = \phi(\overset{\circ}{M}, 2\tau)$ have no common point, likewise $\phi(\overset{\circ}{M}, 2\tau)$ and $\phi\{\phi(\overset{\circ}{M}, 2\tau), \tau\} = \phi(\overset{\circ}{M}, 3\tau)$, and so on. (We have used here the premiss about the law of combination of transformations.) But not all the sets of the sequence $\overset{\circ}{M}, \phi(\overset{\circ}{M}, \tau)$, $\phi(\overset{\circ}{M}, 2\tau),\ \phi(\overset{\circ}{M}, 3\tau),\ \ldots$ can be such that each pair has no common point. For their total volume would be

$$m(\overset{\circ}{M}) + m\{\phi(\overset{\circ}{M}, \tau)\} + m\{\phi(\overset{\circ}{M}, 2\tau)\} + \ldots$$

which, owing to the metrical invariance of the mapping ϕ, equals

$$m(\overset{\circ}{M}) + m(\overset{\circ}{M}) + m(\overset{\circ}{M}) + \ldots,$$

and is infinite. But the total volume must be less than $m(J)$, since all the sets in the sequence, and therefore the sum of the sequence, are subsets of J. We have tacitly assumed that all the sets of the sequence are measurable. This is certainly the case, for they are all one-to-one continuous mappings of the open or closed initial set $\mathring{M}$, and are therefore themselves either open or closed. Such sets are measurable.

In the sequence of sets there is, therefore, at least one pair of sets $\phi(\mathring{M}, v_1\tau)$ and $\phi(\mathring{M}, v_2\tau)$, with $0 \leqslant v_1 < v_2$, which have points in common. Then the following pair of sets also has common points, namely

$$\phi\{\phi(\mathring{M}, v_1\tau), -v_1\tau\} \quad \text{and} \quad \phi\{\phi(\mathring{M}, v_2\tau), -v_1\tau\},$$

and this is the pair

$$\phi(\mathring{M}, v_1\tau - v_1\tau) \quad \text{and} \quad \phi(\mathring{M}, v_2\tau - v_1\tau),$$

or
$$\mathring{M} \quad \text{and} \quad \phi(\mathring{M}, q\tau),$$

where $q = v_2 - v_1 > 0$. This is the statement (a). Evidently the essential point is not whether the initial set is open or closed, but whether all the sets in question are measurable. The proviso was only introduced for the easier formulation of the lemma.

According to the statement (b), if δ is an arbitrary positive constant, then the set A_δ is measurable. We define A_δ as the set of initial points $\mathring{x}$ in J for which all points in the sequence

$$\phi(\mathring{x}, +\tau), \ \phi(\mathring{x}, -\tau), \ \phi(\mathring{x}, +2\tau), \ \phi(\mathring{x}, -2\tau), \ \ldots$$

have a distance greater than δ from $\mathring{x}$.

To prove this we introduce the set $A_\delta(v)$ which consists of all points $\mathring{x}$ in J having the property that the $2v$ image points

$$\phi(\mathring{x}, \pm\tau), \ \phi(\mathring{x}, \pm 2\tau), \ \ldots, \ \phi(\mathring{x}, \pm v\tau)$$

have a distance greater than δ from $\mathring{x}$. Owing to the continuity of the mapping, $A_\delta(v)$ is an open set and is therefore measurable. Now A_δ is evidently the set of points which belong to $A_\delta(1)$ and $A_\delta(2)$ and $A_\delta(3)$ and so on. It is therefore the intersection of all the $A_\delta(v)$, where $v = 1, 2, 3, \ldots$, and the intersection of a denumerable number of measurable sets is also measurable.

According to the statement (c) the set A_δ has measure zero.

The proof is indirect. Suppose, instead, that the statement is false and that A_δ has a positive measure. Suppose that A_δ is contained in the sum of a denumerable set of open spheres of radius ϵ. This set certainly exists. The intersection of each sphere with A_δ is measurable. At least one intersection must have a positive measure, or else A_δ, being the sum of all these intersections, would have zero measure. Let the non-zero intersection be called D and the corresponding sphere be called K.

Then the image sets of D are

$$\phi(D, \pm\tau), \; \phi(D, \pm 2\tau), \; \ldots$$

and these are measurable. For, with any arbitrary integer v,

$$\begin{aligned}
\phi(D, v\tau) &= \phi(A_\delta . K, v\tau) \\
&= \phi(A_\delta, v\tau) . \phi(K, v\tau) \\
&= A_\delta . \phi(K, v\tau)
\end{aligned}$$

since, evidently, $\phi(A_\delta, v\tau) = A_\delta$. Further, the image sets $\phi(K, v\tau)$ are open, because K is open, and consequently they are measurable. Finally, $\phi(D, v\tau)$ is an intersection of measurable sets and is itself measurable.

The generalization of theorem (a) may be applied to the set D, for all the image sets of D in the sequence considered are measurable. This was the essential point in theorem (a). It follows that there is, in the sequence of successive mappings of D

$$\phi(D, \tau), \; \phi(D, 2\tau), \; \phi(D, 3\tau), \; \ldots$$

at least one mapping $\phi(D, q\tau)$ which has a point $\overset{\approx}{x}$ in common with D. Let $\overset{.}{x}$ be the initial point whose image at the time $q\tau$ is the point $\overset{\approx}{x}$, so that

$$\overset{\approx}{x} = \phi(\overset{.}{x}, q\tau), \quad \text{or} \quad \overset{.}{x} = \phi(\overset{\approx}{x}, -q\tau).$$

We now choose a radius ϵ less than $\tfrac{1}{2}\delta$ for the set of spheres which cover A_δ. Then both points $\overset{.}{x}$ and $\overset{\approx}{x}$ lie within the sphere K, whose radius is ϵ, and they are therefore separated by a distance less than δ. Thus the distance between $\overset{.}{x}$ and $\overset{\approx}{x}$ is both greater and less than δ. This contradiction disappears only if we omit the hypothesis $m(D) > 0$. It follows that

$$m(K . A_\delta) = 0.$$

Now K was one of the set of spheres which contain A_δ. We
nclude similarly that

$$m(K_v . A_\delta) = 0, \qquad v = 1, 2, \ldots$$

r all the other covering spheres $K_1, K_2, \ldots$. But

$$A_\delta = K_1 . A_\delta + K_2 . A_\delta + \ldots,$$

d since $\qquad m(A_\delta) \leqslant m(K_1 . A_\delta) + m(K_2 . A_\delta) + \ldots,$

en also $\qquad\qquad\qquad m(A_\delta) = 0.$

is was the statement (c).

Finally, we shall prove the statement (d) that the set of all
e non-recurrence points has zero measure.

The proof is immediate if we represent the set A by

$$A = A_1 + A_{\frac{1}{2}} + A_{\frac{1}{3}} + \ldots.$$

e deduce that

$$m(A) \leqslant m(A_1) + m(A_{\frac{1}{2}}) + m(A_{\frac{1}{3}}) + \ldots = 0,$$

ace each term of the sum on the right-hand side is zero.

This completes the proof of the recurrence theorem for the
ture. A similar proof applies to the past. The significance of
e theorem, discussed at the beginning of this section, is that it
ves a description of the evolution of a mechanical system whose
tential U permits the existence of an invariant set J of positive
ite measure.

8. We shall now sum up the work so far. Liouville's theorem,
hich we have found to be an important lemma, states that the
hase-flow" ϕ of a mechanical system is metrically invariant if
the forces are independent of the velocities. An equivalent
atement is that the functional determinant satisfies $\Delta(\overset{\circ}{x}, t) \equiv 1$.
he recurrence theorem holds for metrically invariant, stationary
ase-flows—provided, however, that there is an invariant sub-
gion J in phase-space with a positive, finite measure. This will
rtainly be the case if the potential has a minimum, but not
the potential has no lower bound. Roughly speaking, the
currence theorem states that almost every streamline in J comes

arbitrarily close to its initial point an infinite number times.

9. We shall add a critical comment about the recurrence theorem. The latter seems to make a statement about the behaviour of the system in the large, or about its behaviour as $t \to \infty$. Now the theorem may have absolute validity for the mathematical model, but it is not at once certain whether it is applicable to or valid for the real system.

From the scientific point of view there is not much significance in the mathematical statement that the moving point x approaches arbitrarily closely again to the initial point $\overset{\circ}{x}$ after a long enough time. More significant is the answer to the question: How much time will pass before the moving point x enters again into a sphere of arbitrarily given radius ϵ, with its centre at the initial point $\overset{\circ}{x}$? In any application, the radius ϵ must be chosen to correspond to the observational accuracy, so that the interior of the sphere represents those states of system which are equivalent for practical purposes.

We can make a crude estimate of the order of magnitude of the recurrence time in the following way. Let the positive constant τ be chosen to be small but nevertheless sufficiently large that K and $\phi(K, \tau)$ have no points in common. Let the set $\phi(K, q\tau)$ be the first in the sequence

$$\phi(K, \tau), \ \phi(K, 2\tau), \ \phi(K, 3\tau), \ \dots,$$

which has a non-zero intersection with K. The considerations expressed in Section 7 evidently show that

$$q \leqslant \frac{m(J)}{m(K)}.$$

Let $\overset{2}{x}$ be a point of the intersection $K . \phi(K, q\tau)$; we consider it to be the image point, at time $q\tau$, of the original point $\overset{\circ}{x}$ in K, and we assume the initial state of the system to be represented by $\overset{\circ}{x}$ and not by $\overset{\circ}{x}$. The assumption is justified, ϵ having been chosen so small that the states $\overset{\circ}{x}$ and $\overset{\circ}{x}$ are, in practice, indistinguishable. The image point $\overset{2}{x}$ is therefore inside a sphere of radius 2ϵ around the initial point $\overset{\circ}{x}$. The corresponding recurrence time is less than $\tau\{m(J)/m(K)\}$. If $\phi(K,\tau)$ were also a sphere of radius ϵ, then we should have that

$$\tau \approx \frac{2\epsilon}{|\dot{x}|} = \frac{2\epsilon}{\sqrt{\left[\sum_{1}^{m}\{f_i(\overset{0}{\dot{x}})\}^2\right]}}.$$

Now the "average shape" of the image region $\phi(K,\tau)$ is, in fact, spherical. We therefore extend the use of this value of τ to the general case, and obtain an approximate upper bound for the recurrence time which equals

$$\frac{m(J)}{m(K)}\frac{2\epsilon}{\sqrt{\left[\sum_{1}^{m}\{f_i(\overset{0}{\dot{x}})\}^2\right]}}.$$

It seems to be a very hard problem to estimate the recurrence time accurately. But only a solution of the problem can give a significance to scientific applications of the recurrence theorem.

We may add that, in practice, real systems are never self-contained mechanically: there are always small outside disturbances acting on them. The assumptions of the recurrence theorem are therefore never, strictly speaking, fulfilled. This circumstance can be taken into account in two ways. The small disturbances may add up to significant disturbances after a long time (they may, but need not, do so). The recurrence theorem will be applicable if, and only if, the recurrence time is small compared with the least interval during which the disturbing forces can have an appreciable influence on the system. One should, further, attempt to generalize the theorem (and its scientific application, in particular) by considering the disturbing forces explicitly, as it seems this has not been done yet. But in any case, when we deal with such general theorems, we must always bear in mind the distinction between reality and our mental picture of it, and remember how far that model is applicable. The limits of the applicability are, themselves, rather vague.

Examples

1. What connexion is there between the first integrals of the equations of motion and the laws of conservation? Is there an integral which corresponds to the theorem of the centroid?

2. Is there a "formal energy theorem" for time-dependent potentials, possibly one of the form

$$T + U = \int \frac{\partial U}{\partial t}\, dt + \text{const ?}$$

3. The order of the system of differential equations may be reduced by one if all the right-hand sides are time independent. Why is this so? What disadvantage do we get in exchange?

4. A harmonic oscillator has the equation of motion

$$\ddot{x} = -x.$$

Integrate the equation by successive approximations, with the initial conditions $x(0) = \overset{\circ}{x}$, $\dot{x}(0) = \overset{\circ}{u}$. Express the resulting power series by means of known elementary functions.

5. Suppose that the differential equation $\ddot{x} = f(x)$ has the general solution

$$x = \phi(\overset{\circ}{u}, \overset{\circ}{x}, t), \quad u = \dot{\phi}(\overset{\circ}{u}, \overset{\circ}{x}, t).$$

What is the general solution of

$$\ddot{x} = \alpha^2 f(x), \quad \alpha = \text{const ?}$$

Apply the result to the equation

$$\ddot{x} = -\alpha^2 x.$$

6. Use the example of a freely falling particle to elucidate the content of the theorem which states that the inverse functions of the solution functions are first integrals.

7. What gaps are there in this "proof" of Liouville's theorem? The total time derivative of $\psi(x, t)$ is zero, hence

$$\frac{\partial \psi}{\partial t} + \sum_{1}^{m} \frac{\partial \psi}{\partial x_j}\, \dot{x}_j = 0.$$

But

$$\dot{x}_j = f_j(x, t),$$

so that

$$\frac{\partial \psi}{\partial t} + \sum_{1}^{m} \frac{\partial \psi}{\partial x_j} f_j = 0.$$

8. Why is the solution of Liouville's equation unique with given initial conditions?

9. Elucidate the content of the recurrence theorem by means of the example of two independent harmonic oscillators with equations of motion

$$\ddot{x} = -(2\pi)^2 x, \quad \ddot{y} = -(2\pi v)^2 y, \quad v = \text{const} > 0,$$

which are regarded as components of a single system. (For a solution of these equations of motion, see Example 4 or 5, or Chapter V, § 4.10.)

10. Why must the number τ be introduced in a formulation of the recurrence theorem? Why is its particular value immaterial, provided it is known to be positive (or negative)?

11. Compare the recurrence time of a harmonic oscillator with the upper bound given in the text.

12. Discuss qualitatively how the accuracy of the estimate for the recurrence time, given in the text, depends on the number n of particles.

Comments and References to the Literature

Our discussion is restricted to Cartesian coordinates. One could extend it all to general coordinates, but would not learn much further in doing so. Liouville's theorem can be proved for general Hamiltonian coordinates in a way completely analogous to that in our text.

Newton's equations of motion, and references to their empirical foundations, are given in every textbook of theoretical physics. The foundations are clearly set out (even in places where one's own opinion differs from the author's) in the book by Mach:

[11] MACH, E., *Die Mechanik in ihrer geschichtlichen Entwicklung*, Leipzig, 1901.

Of the numerous works on differential equations, we only refer to Kamke's:

[12] KAMKE, E., *Differentialgleichungen reeller Funktionen*, Leipzig, 1930.

Kamke employs the term "integral" in a sense different from ours. He uses it to denote what we call a solution function.

Poincaré's proof of his recurrence theorem is given in his work:

[13] POINCARÉ, H., *Les méthodes nouvelles de la mécanique céleste*, Paris, 1893.

The proof is mainly correct, but not in all its details.

This is inevitable, for Poincaré did not have the concept of Lebesgue measure available to him. Only when the concept is used can we be sure of the measurability of all the point sets which occur, and this is its only purpose.

Carathéodory made the corresponding corrections in Poincaré's proof:

[14] CARATHÉODORY, C., *Über den Wiederkehrsatz von Poincaré*, in *Sitzungsberichte der Preussischen Akademie der Wissenschaften*, 1919, pp. 580–584.

CHAPTER IV

STELLAR SYSTEMS AS ASSEMBLIES OF GRAVITATING PARTICLES

1. Newton's law of gravitation

1. In this chapter we shall describe real stellar systems by means of model systems of gravitating particles. A particle j will be assumed to act on a particle i with a force $\boldsymbol{k}_{ij}$, whose magnitude is given by

$$|\boldsymbol{k}_{ij}| = G\frac{m_i m_j}{|\boldsymbol{r}_j - \boldsymbol{r}_i|^2},$$

where $\boldsymbol{r}_i$ and $\boldsymbol{r}_j$ are the position vectors of the two particles, m_i and m_j their masses, and G the constant of gravitation. The unit vector parallel to the direction from i to j is

$$\frac{\boldsymbol{r}_j - \boldsymbol{r}_i}{|\boldsymbol{r}_j - \boldsymbol{r}_i|}.$$

The force can therefore be expressed by

$$\boldsymbol{k}_{ij} = G\frac{m_i m_j}{|\boldsymbol{r}_j - \boldsymbol{r}_i|^3}(\boldsymbol{r}_j - \boldsymbol{r}_i),$$

and Newton's equations of motion read

$$m_i \ddot{\boldsymbol{r}}_i = G\sum_{\substack{j=1 \\ j \neq i}}^{n} \frac{m_i m_j}{|\boldsymbol{r}_j - \boldsymbol{r}_i|^3}(\boldsymbol{r}_j - \boldsymbol{r}_i), \qquad i = 1, 2, \ldots, n.$$

It is easily verified that the right-hand sides can be expressed as gradients of

$$-U = G\sum_{1 \leqslant i < j \leqslant n} \frac{m_i m_j}{|\boldsymbol{r}_j - \boldsymbol{r}_i|}$$

$$= \tfrac{1}{2}G\sum_{\substack{i,j=1 \\ i \neq j}}^{n} \frac{m_i m_j}{|\boldsymbol{r}_j - \boldsymbol{r}_i|},$$

and that the equations of motion may be written

$$m_i \ddot{x}_i = -\frac{\partial U}{\partial x_i}, \qquad i = 1, 2, \ldots, n,$$

with similar equations for y_i and z_i.

2. We now ask how far these equations satisfy the assumptions on which we based our general mechanics in Chapter III. It is evident that they do not fulfil all the conditions of the fundamental theorems of existence and uniqueness, given in III, § 2. For example, there is no bound on the right-hand sides of the above set of differential equations; arbitrarily large forces can arise when two particles approach one another sufficiently closely. (The unbounded functions u_i, v_i, w_i in the equations of III, § 2.1 cause no trouble as can easily be shown by means of successive approximations.)

This difficulty can be removed most simply if we remember that the real stars are not mass-points but are, to a good enough approximation, spheres of relatively small, but finite, radius. If two stars approach each other so closely as to collide, then the idealized representation of the system by mass-points is certainly no longer applicable.

It is not possible to predict what will happen to the two stars in such a case. Every simple law of force is therefore inapplicable for small separations $|\mathbf{r}_i - \mathbf{r}_j|$ of two stars, and so we are free to replace the Newtonian law, which is false, by another law which, although false, is more convenient mathematically. Two conditions must be fulfilled in order that a useful mechanical theory may be built up in spite of the false hypothesis. First, the stars must have diameters which are very small compared with their mutual distances, so that close encounters are very rare events. Second, the number of stars must be so large that the evolution of the system as a whole (at least for a sufficiently long time) remains unaffected by the accidental collision of two stars; in other words, the calculation of the evolution shall not essentially depend on whether the description of the motions of these two stars is correct or false.

We therefore change the law of gravitation for very small distances in some way which will make it satisfy all the

E

conditions required in III, § 2. The gravitational potential U then becomes a bounded function of the position vectors $r_1, \ldots, r_n$, thus satisfying all the theorems of Chapter III concerning systems of ordinary differential equations. In particular the conservation laws of mechanics will hold, and so will Liouville's theorem concerning the metrical invariance of the phase flow in R^{6n}.

3. We shall now interpolate a few theorems concerning the gravitation of mass distributions in space, with a view to their use later.

We consider, first of all, the force exerted by n particles, of mass $m_1, \ldots, m_n$, with vector coordinates $r_1, \ldots, r_n$, on an $(n+1)^{th}$ particle of unit mass at the point r. The $(n+1)$ positions are, of course, assumed to be distinct. The force is called the field intensity at the point r due to the system of the first n particles, and is evidently given by

$$F = -G \sum_{i=1}^{n} m_i \frac{r - r_i}{|r - r_i|^3}.$$

If V is the potential

$$V = G \sum_{i=1}^{n} \frac{m_i}{|r - r_i|},$$

the field intensity $F = (F_x, F_y, F_z)$ can be expressed as the negative gradient of the scalar function V, so that

$$F_x = -\frac{\partial V}{\partial x}, \quad \text{etc.}$$

The potential V is clearly different from the potential function

$$U = -G \sum_{1 \leqslant i < j \leqslant n} \frac{m_i m_j}{|r_i - r_j|}.$$

The latter describes the mutual interactions of all the particles considered, while V refers solely to their influence on an $(n+1)^{th}$ particle of unit mass. If this particle has mass m, rather than unit mass, its "potential" energy with respect to the first n particles is given by mV.

A completely analogous definition may be given for the intensity and potential due to spatially extended masses by using elements dm of mass, instead of particles with mass m_i, and integrals, instead of sums. For the sake of simplicity we shall assume, unless the contrary is stated, that the bodies considered have only a finite extent, that the distribution of mass in them can be described by means of a mass density $\rho(\boldsymbol{r})$ having continuous derivatives with respect to the coordinates, and that this density and its derivatives decrease to zero as the boundary of the body is approached. Thus $\rho(\boldsymbol{r})$ may be considered to be a bounded and differentiable function of the position vector $\boldsymbol{r}$, with bounded and continuous derivatives in the whole of R^3. Generally $\rho(\boldsymbol{r})$ is positive only in a bounded region of R^3, and is zero elsewhere.

We then represent the field intensity due to the body at the point r by

$$F_x(\boldsymbol{r}) = -G \iiint_{R^3} \frac{\rho(\xi, \eta, \zeta)}{r^2} \frac{x - \xi}{r} \, d\xi \, d\eta \, d\zeta,$$

where
$$r = \sqrt{[(x - \xi)^2 + (y - \eta)^2 + (z - \zeta)^2]},$$

with similar expressions for F_y and F_z, and the potential V by

$$V(\boldsymbol{r}) = G \iiint_{R^3} \frac{\rho(\xi, \eta, \zeta)}{r} \, d\xi \, d\eta \, d\zeta.$$

The expressions are meaningful even when the reference point $\boldsymbol{r}$ lies inside the mass distribution, in other words the integrals converge even for such points $\boldsymbol{r}$. Both the intensity and the potential are functions of $\boldsymbol{r}$ which are bounded and continuously differentiable in all R^3. In particular, both functions vary continuously when the reference point moves through the boundary of the body. Further the relations

$$F_x = -\frac{\partial V}{\partial x}, \quad \text{etc.}$$

are satisfied everywhere in R^3.

The derivatives satisfy Poisson's equation

$$-\left(\frac{\partial F_x}{\partial x} + \frac{\partial F_y}{\partial y} + \frac{\partial F_z}{\partial z}\right) \equiv \frac{\partial^2 V}{\partial x^2} + \frac{\partial^2 V}{\partial y^2} + \frac{\partial^2 V}{\partial z^2} = 4\pi G\rho,$$

which takes the form

$$\frac{d^2 V}{dr^2} + \frac{2}{r} \frac{dV}{dr} = 4\pi G\rho,$$

for distributions with spherical symmetry. In this case both $\rho = \rho(r)$ and $V = V(r)$ are functions only of the radial distance r. The left-hand side may also be written as

$$\frac{1}{r^2}\frac{\mathrm{d}}{\mathrm{d}r}\left(r^2\frac{\mathrm{d}V}{\mathrm{d}r}\right).$$

We deduce, on integration, that a uniform spherical shell exerts no gravitational force on a particle in its interior, and that the gravitational force which it exerts at an outside point is the same as that which would be exerted, at that point, by a particle of equal mass at the centre of the shell. Corresponding results apply to the potential, which is constant inside the shell. An arbitrary value can be assigned to it there, as a constant of integration, the value zero being chosen as a rule.

It follows that the potential energy U may be expressed, for a distribution of material with spherical symmetry, by

$$\mathrm{d}U = -G\frac{m(r)\,\mathrm{d}m(r)}{r},$$

where

$$m(r) = 4\pi\int_0^r \rho(s)\,s^2\,\mathrm{d}s$$

denotes the mass within the sphere of radius r.

2. The theorems of E. Hopf

1. We now return to the mechanics of a system of gravitating particles. In III, § 3, we were able, with certain assumptions, to describe the evolution of a mechanical system in the large in the following approximate way. We found that the system will be "quasi-periodic" in almost all cases, or, in other words, that it will come arbitrarily close to its initial state again and again. The decisive assumption was that there should be, in R^{6n}, an invariant region J, with a positive and finite measure, which is invariant with respect to the phase flows ϕ. The question now arises whether such a region J exists when the flow is determined by Newtonian forces of gravitation.

Nobody has yet succeeded in describing such a region J, nor does it seem likely that this will ever be done. For, in order to make the description in practice, we must choose two numbers α

and β, as in III, § 2, which are such that the set of all points in phase space satisfying

$$\alpha < H < \beta$$

forms a region J of the type required. Here H again denotes the energy function

$$H = \tfrac{1}{2} \sum_{1}^{n} m_i(u_i^2 + v_i^2 + w_i^2) + U(\boldsymbol{r}_1, \ldots, \boldsymbol{r}_n).$$

In the case of the ideal Newtonian potential all such regions extend to infinity. For $U \to -\infty$ when two particles approach more and more closely, so that the kinetic energy and also the velocity components may take arbitrarily large values. It turns out that these regions have an infinite content and therefore do not satisfy the requirements of Poincaré's theorem.

But in § 1.2 we altered the ideal Newtonian potential in such a way that it remained bounded even when the distances between particles became very small. The conditions of the recurrence theorem are then formally satisfied. We can, for the sake of the argument, choose to make a change such that the potential $U_{ij}(|\boldsymbol{r}_i - \boldsymbol{r}_j|)$, between the particles i and j, becomes a monotonically increasing function of the distance of separation $|\boldsymbol{r}_i - \boldsymbol{r}_j|$ and takes the value zero when $|\boldsymbol{r}_i - \boldsymbol{r}_j| = 0$. We now choose $\alpha = 0$ and $\beta > 0$, but small enough to make the region $H < \beta$ bounded. This choice is possible in any case, and we have thus defined an invariant region having the desired properties.

However, this method of treating the problem leads to consequences which cannot be reconciled with the known behaviour of real stellar systems. To simplify matters, we assume that all the stellar masses and diameters are equal. Let δ be the distance below which we must change the form of the gravitational potential, say, a stellar diameter. If we wish to be certain that $m(J) < \infty$ we are forced to choose β to be very small, as can be demonstrated, so small, in fact, that at least two particles must be separated by a distance not larger than $n\delta/(n-2)$. Some of the particles would therefore be crowded together to such an extent that the corresponding real stars would nearly touch. The proof of this statement is simple but rather lengthy. The result will not be used again and we shall omit the proof.

Thus it is, in a sense, impossible to satisfy the fundamental condition of the recurrence theorem that there shall be, in phase space, an invariant subset of positive and finite measure. The recurrence theorem itself is therefore not applicable, and we ask whether it can be suitably generalized. The theorems of Hopf provide an answer to our query.

2. As in the case of the recurrence theorem we shall consider the steady flow ϕ of an incompressible substrate in phase space R^n. The definition of a recurrence point is the same as in Poincaré's theorem.

A point $\overset{\circ}{x} \in R^m$ is called a recurrence point with respect to the future if it is a point of accumulation of the sequence

$$\phi(\overset{\circ}{x}, \tau),\ \phi(\overset{\circ}{x}, 2\tau),\ \phi(\overset{\circ}{x}, 3\tau),\ \ldots$$

for any fixed positive τ. If $\overset{\circ}{x}$ is a point of accumulation of the sequence

$$\phi(\overset{\circ}{x}, -\sigma),\ \phi(\overset{\circ}{x}, -2\sigma),\ \phi(\overset{\circ}{x}, -3\sigma),\ \ldots$$

for any positive σ, then $\overset{\circ}{x}$ is a point of accumulation with respect to the past.

Further, we shall say that a point $\overset{\circ}{x}$ is a point of escape with respect to the future or the past if the distances from $\overset{\circ}{x}$ of the points in the sequence

$$\phi(\overset{\circ}{x}, \tau),\ \phi(\overset{\circ}{x}, 2\tau),\ \phi(\overset{\circ}{x}, 3\tau),\ \ldots$$

or in the sequence

$$\phi(\overset{\circ}{x}, -\sigma),\ \phi(\overset{\circ}{x}, -2\sigma),\ \phi(\overset{\circ}{x}, -3\sigma),\ \ldots, \quad \text{respectively,}$$

increase beyond all bounds.

It is evident that if *one* point on a streamline has the property of being a recurrence point or a point of escape with respect to a particular direction in space, then all points on the line have that property.

Hopf's First Theorem states that, except for a set of zero measure, all points in R^m are either recurrence points or points of escape. This applies to both future and past.

The significance of this result for mechanics is that, apart from negligibly rare exceptions, either the evolution of a system is quasi-periodic, or the system disintegrates—that is, at least one particle leaves the system for infinity. This last statement may be justified by noting that, if $\overset{o}{x}$ is a point of escape, at least one coordinate of the moving point x must tend to infinity. This coordinate cannot be one of the velocity components, for we have altered the gravitational potential to make the potential function U bounded. Because of the energy theorem the function T of the kinetic energy is then also bounded, and so are all the velocity components. It must therefore be one of the position coordinates which tends to infinity.

If the mass centre of the system is taken as origin of the coordinates, so that

$$\sum_1^n m_i \mathbf{r}_i(t) = 0,$$

for all times t, we may further conclude that if *one* particle escapes to infinity, then at least another particle escapes there as well. This is necessarily required by the above equation. If two particles escape to infinity it follows again, from the theorem of the centroid, that they will approach, asymptotically, the same straight line through the centroid (on opposite sides, of course). Their distances from the centroid become asymptotically equal as functions of time. Now the approach to a straight line like this can occur only with very special initial conditions. It follows that, when a system disintegrates, at least three bodies will, as a rule, escape to infinity.

We can see, from these considerations, what are the limitations of the approach based on particle mechanics. Suppose that a system of stars loses two or three, or, for that matter, a few hundred members. It is unlikely that the loss will have a noticeable effect on its structure or on its evolution. In fact, particle mechanics takes account of such superfluous details, but it gives no information about the remaining, say, $10^6 - 3$ stars, in which we are interested.

Nevertheless we consider that Hopf's generalization of Poincaré's theorem is essentially an important result, and we shall sketch out its proof, which is quite analogous to the proof of Poincaré's theorem.

3. Let K be a sphere in R^m, with centre at the origin and radius r. Let $A(r)$ be the set of all initial points $\overset{o}{x}$ in K which

are not recurrence points with respect to the future, say, and whose streamlines lie entirely within K for $t > 0$. As in the case of the recurrence theorem it may be shown that $A(r)$ has the measure zero. Now let A be the set of all points $\overset{\circ}{x}$ which are neither points of recurrence nor of escape, then evidently

$$A = A(1) + A(2) + A(3) + \dots.$$

Every term on the right-hand side has measure zero and so has the sum A. This proves our statement. The theorem and proof apply to the past as well as to the future.

4. The result we have just found leads us to ask whether it is at all possible that a streamline should have different descriptions with respect to the past and to the future. For example, can a given initial point be a point of escape with respect to the past and a recurrence point with respect to the future, or conversely? This seems to be unlikely, *a priori*, since neither direction in time is preferred by Newton's equations. (When the time variable t is replaced by $-t$, the equations are transformed into themselves.) Hopf's Second Theorem confirms this, for it states that, except for a set of measure zero, all initial points which are points of escape or recurrence points with respect to the past are also, respectively, points of escape or recurrence points with respect to the future.

The theorem has the following significance in the mechanics of stellar systems. Apart from insignificant exceptional cases, a stellar system can disintegrate into sub-systems if, and only if, it was originally constituted out of sub-systems.

5. We shall only give an outline of the proof. Let $F \subset R^m$ be any set of points of escape with respect to the future and let it have a positive measure. (If such a set does not exist, then read "past" for "future". If F does not exist in either case there is nothing left to prove, for then "almost all" points are recurrence points with respect to both directions in time.) Let $\overset{\circ}{x}$ be a point of F, and $S.F$ the intersection of F with a sphere S, centre $\overset{\circ}{x}$. Let the radius of S be so small, that for any given τ, none of the image sets

$$\phi(S.F, \tau), \ \phi(S.F, 2\tau), \ \dots$$

have a point in common with $S.F$. There must be such a sphere, or else $\overset{0}{x}$ would be a recurrence point. No pair in the sequence of sets therefore have a point in common, and this applies also to the sets

$$\dots,\ \phi(S.F,\ -2\tau),\ \phi(S.F,\ -\tau),\ S.F,\ \phi(S.F,\tau),\ \dots.$$

We now prove that, at most, a subset $F' \subset F.S$, with measure $m(F') = 0$, is formed by the points $\overset{0}{x}$ whose image points

$$\phi(\overset{0}{x},\ -\tau),\ \phi(\overset{0}{x},\ -2\tau),\ \phi(\overset{0}{x},\ -3\tau),\ \dots$$

all lie within a sphere K of arbitrary radius r about the origin. For, if $m(F')$ were greater than zero, then an integer q would exist such that F' and $\phi(F',\ -q\tau)$ have a common point. (The argument is the same as in the proof of the recurrence theorem in III, § 3.7.) But F' and $\phi(F',\ -q\tau)$ are, respectively, subsets of F and $\phi(F,\ -q\tau)$, and cannot have points in common. It follows that $m(F')$ cannot be positive, and that almost all points of $\phi(S.F,\ -v\tau)$ are outside the arbitrarily large sphere K for sufficiently large v. Hence almost all points of F are points of escape with respect to the past.

The argument from the past to the future is similar. It only remains to be proved that F can be covered by a denumerable set of suitable spheres S. The basic ideas of this proof occur also in the proof of the recurrence theorem, and may be carried over from there without difficulty. We shall therefore not go into any further details.

3. Lagrange's Identity

1. According to Hopf's First Theorem there are, effectively, only two possible ways of evolution of a stellar system, recurrence or disintegration. How can we decide which of these occurs?

A partial answer to this question is given, in the case of systems of gravitating particles, by Lagrange's Identity, which states the following. Let U be the potential energy function, T the kinetic energy and J the function

$$J \equiv \sum_1^n m_i \mathbf{r}_i^2 = \sum_1^n m_i \,|\, r_i \,|^2$$

of the independent variables $r_1, r_2, \ldots, r_n$. If the independent variables in these functions are replaced by any solution $r_i = r_i(t)$ of the Newtonian equations of motion, then

$$\tfrac{1}{2}\ddot{J} = 2T + U$$

for all times t.

To prove this we differentiate J, regarded as a function of t, twice with respect to t, and obtain

$$\tfrac{1}{2}\ddot{J} = \sum_1^n m_i \dot{r}_i^2 + \sum_1^n m_i r_i . \ddot{r}_i.$$

The first term on the right-hand side equals $2T$. The second can be transformed by means of the equations of motion

$$m_i \ddot{x}_i = -\frac{\partial U}{\partial x_i}, \quad \text{etc.}$$

to give

$$\sum_1^n m_i \ddot{r}_i . \, r_i = \sum_1^n (m_i \ddot{x}_i x_i + m_i \ddot{y}_i y_i + m_i \ddot{z}_i z_i)$$

$$= -\sum_1^n \left(\frac{\partial U}{\partial x_i} x_i + \frac{\partial U}{\partial y_i} y_i + \frac{\partial U}{\partial z_i} z_i \right).$$

Now

$$U = -G \sum_{i<j} \frac{m_i m_j}{|\, r_i - r_j \,|}$$

is a homogeneous function of order -1 in the $3n$ variables $x_1, \ldots, z_n$. Hence, for any set of $x_1, \ldots, z_n$ and for $\alpha \neq 0$

$$U(\alpha x_1, \ldots, \alpha z_n) \equiv \frac{1}{\alpha} U(x_1, \ldots, z_n).$$

We differentiate this identity with respect to α at $\alpha = 1$, and obtain the (special) Eulerian Identity

$$\sum_1^n \left[\frac{\partial U}{\partial x_i} x_i + \frac{\partial U}{\partial y_i} y_i + \frac{\partial U}{\partial z_i} z_i \right] \equiv -U.$$

We therefore find, from the expression for $\tfrac{1}{2}\ddot{J}$, that

$$\tfrac{1}{2}\ddot{J} = 2T + U,$$

as stated.

2. A stellar system which does not disintegrate will be said to be stable. A simple combination of Lagrange's Identity with the

energy theorem $$T + U = E$$

(III, § 1.4) yields Jacobi's criterion of stability, which states that a system is unstable if its total energy E is positive.

For from these two relations it follows immediately that

$$\tfrac{1}{2}\ddot{J} = E + T,$$

or, equally, $$\tfrac{1}{2}\ddot{J} = 2E - U.$$

Since U is essentially negative we deduce from the last equation that, when $E > 0$ and $t \geqslant 0$,

$$\ddot{J} > 4E,$$

$$\dot{J} > 4Et + \dot{J}_{t=0},$$

$$J > 2Et^2 + t\dot{J}_{t=0} + J_{t=0},$$

so that $$J \to \infty \quad \text{as} \quad t \to \infty.$$

At least one $|\boldsymbol{r}_i|$ must therefore increase beyond all bounds, and at least one particle must finally leave the system (since we made the origin coincident with the centroid and can measure the position vectors from there).

A combination of the inequality $\ddot{J} > 4E$ with Hopf's First Theorem makes it possible to show that, when $E = 0$, the system is unstable in the great majority of cases. This statement, however, has hardly any significance from the scientific point of view, since it is, in principle, impossible to make empirically an absolutely exact determination of the total energy (to see whether it is exactly zero or not). For this reason we shall omit the proof.

Up to the present no satisfactory criterion has been found, for systems with negative total energy, to decide between the two possibilities of periodicity and disintegration. It appears to be one of the most important unsolved problems in the mechanics of stellar systems to discover such a criterion—not only from the purely theoretical standpoint, but also with a view to an application to real systems of stars.

3. As an application we shall use Jacobi's criterion of stability in the following explicit form. The system has the (instantaneous)

kinetic energy
$$T = \tfrac{1}{2} \sum_1^n m_i \dot{\boldsymbol{r}}_i^2$$

$$= \tfrac{1}{2} M \overline{v^2},$$

where $M = \sum_1^n m_i$ is its total mass and

$$\overline{v^2} = \frac{1}{M} \sum_1^n m_i \dot{\boldsymbol{r}}_i^2$$

denotes the weighted mean square speed of all the stars with respect to the centre of mass of the cluster. As a rule we can only measure the radial component R of this speed for a few stars (radial, that is, with respect to the direction of the Sun). We now assume that on the average the two transverse components, which we cannot measure, are about equal to the radial velocity R, and put

$$\overline{v^2} \approx 3 \overline{R^2}$$

and
$$T \approx \tfrac{3}{2} M \overline{R^2}.$$

According to § 1.1 the (instantaneous) gravitational potential U is given by

$$U = - \tfrac{1}{2} G \sum_{\substack{i,j=1 \\ i \neq j}}^n \frac{m_i m_j}{|\boldsymbol{r}_j - \boldsymbol{r}_i|}.$$

Let $\bar{r}$ stand for the weighted harmonic mean of all the distances $|\boldsymbol{r}_j - \boldsymbol{r}_i|$ between stars, defined by

$$\frac{1}{\bar{r}} \sum_{\substack{i,j=1 \\ i \neq j}}^n m_i m_j = \sum_{\substack{i,j=1 \\ i \neq j}}^n \frac{m_i m_j}{|\boldsymbol{r}_i - \boldsymbol{r}_j|}.$$

Now
$$\sum_{\substack{i,j=1 \\ i \neq j}}^n m_i m_j = \sum_{i=1}^n m_i \sum_{j=1}^n m_j - \sum_{k=1}^n m_k^2$$

and
$$\sum_{k=1}^n m_k^2 \leqslant \max_{k=1,\dots,n} m_k \cdot \sum_{i=1}^n m_i$$

$$= M \cdot \max m_k \ll M^2,$$

so that

$$\frac{M^2}{\bar{r}} \approx \sum_{\substack{i,j=1\\i \neq j}}^{n} \frac{m_i m_j}{|\,\boldsymbol{r}_i - \boldsymbol{r}_j\,|},$$

$$U \approx -\frac{1}{2}\frac{GM^2}{\bar{r}},$$

$$E \approx \frac{3}{2}M\overline{\dot{R}^2} - \frac{1}{2}\frac{GM^2}{\bar{r}}.$$

The condition of stability $E < 0$ now yields

$$\frac{GM}{\bar{r}} > 3\overline{\dot{R}^2}.$$

If the system is stable this inequality must hold. It can be interpreted as a relation between the average potential and kinetic energies of a star.

In the case of a system with spherical symmetry we may write $\bar{r} = \alpha r_*$. Here α is a positive number, which is usually of order unity; obviously it is, however, much smaller for strongly concentrated systems.

4. In the case of a system of spherical symmetry we may add this interpretation of the above criterion. We divide the inequality by $(4\pi/3)\,r_*^2$ and find

$$\frac{GM}{(4\pi/3)\,r_*^3\,\alpha} > \frac{9}{4\pi}\frac{\overline{\dot{R}^2}}{r_*^2},$$

then introduce the mean density

$$\bar{\rho} = \frac{M}{(4\pi/3)\,r_*^3}$$

and obtain

$$\sqrt{\left(\frac{\alpha}{G\bar{\rho}}\right)} < \sqrt{\left(\frac{4\pi}{3}\right)}\frac{r_*}{\sqrt{\overline{\dot{v}^2}}} \approx \frac{2r_*}{\sqrt{\overline{\dot{v}^2}}}.$$

Both sides of this inequality have the dimension of a time. The "time scale" on the left is evidently determined by the mechanical conditions of the system, namely the mass distribution and gravitation. The time scale on the right is determined geometrically and kinematically, namely by the diameter of the system and mean speed of the stars. It is, in fact, equal to the time which would be needed by a star moving uniformly in a radial direction to traverse the system.

We can now state the criterion in the following form: If the system is stable, its mechanical time scale is at most equal to its kinematic scale.

5. Finally we can use the criterion to estimate the masses of real systems with spherical symmetry. Conditions for this application are, first, that the systems can, with sufficient approximation, be considered to be mechanically self-contained and, second, that they are stable. The first assumption is probably permissible for globular clusters and clusters of galaxies, but undoubtedly not for open clusters. The second assumption seems less plausible even for the former systems and we shall use it as a working hypothesis. It follows at first that

$$M > 3\alpha \frac{r_* \overline{R^2}}{G}.$$

We now choose the parsec as our unit of length, 10^6 years ($= Z$) as our unit of time, and the solar mass $\odot = 2 \times 10^{33}$ g as the unit of mass. We have that, to within 2 per cent,

$$1 \text{ km/s} = 1 \text{ pc}/Z.$$

The gravitational constant G equals $\frac{1}{233}$ in these units. We obtain

$$M > 700\alpha r_* \overline{R^2} \ [\odot]$$

as a lower bound for the mass of the system.

If we assume the following average values for globular clusters

$$r_* \approx 30 \text{ [pc]}, \quad \overline{R^2} \approx 70 \text{ [km}^2\text{s}^{-2}\text{]}, \text{ and } \alpha \approx 1,$$

we find, for the mass, that

$$M > 1{\cdot}5 \times 10^6 \ [\odot].$$

From the data for a typical cluster of galaxies

$$r_* \approx 5 \times 10^5 \text{ [pc]}, \quad \overline{R^2} \approx 6 \times 10^5 \text{ [km}^2\text{s}^{-2}\text{]}, \quad \alpha \approx 1$$

it follows that

$$M > 2{\cdot}2 \times 10^{14} \ [\odot].$$

If there are 1000 galaxies in a cluster, a single galaxy in it must have, on the average, at least a mass of $2 \times 10^{11} \ [\odot]$.

These values are smaller the more strongly concentrated are the systems.

The estimates hold good provided there is stability. Systems having masses much smaller than our estimates are unstable, *ceteris paribus.*

4. The virial theorem

1. In the case of stable systems Lagrange's Identity

$$\tfrac{1}{2}\ddot{J} = E + T$$

has important consequences. On integrating it with respect to the time and then dividing by $t(>0)$ we find that

$$\frac{1}{2}\frac{\dot{J} - \dot{J}_{t=0}}{t} = \frac{E \cdot t}{t} + \frac{1}{t}\int_0^t T(\tau)\,\mathrm{d}\tau.$$

The left-hand side

$$\frac{1}{t}\sum_1^n m_i\{\boldsymbol{r}_i(t)\cdot\dot{\boldsymbol{r}}_i(t) - \boldsymbol{r}_i(0)\cdot\dot{\boldsymbol{r}}_i(0)\}$$

tends to zero as $t \to \infty$, since the coordinates and the velocity components are bounded functions of the time. It follows immediately that there exists a limit

$$\hat{T} = \lim_{t\to\infty}\frac{1}{t}\int_0^t T(\tau)\,\mathrm{d}\tau,$$

which is the "time average" of the kinetic energy, and equals $-E$.

We now deduce from the energy theorem

$$T + U = E$$

that there also exists a time average $\hat{U}$ of the potential energy (or of the potential) U and find that its value is

$$\hat{U} = E - \hat{T} = 2E.$$

The two statements

$$\hat{T} = -E, \quad \hat{U} = 2E$$

will be called the "virial theorem", in accordance with the usual practice. (The sum

$$\sum_i \left(x_i\frac{\partial U}{\partial x_i} + y_i\frac{\partial U}{\partial y_i} + z_i\frac{\partial U}{\partial z_i}\right)$$

is also called "virial" occasionally. It occurred in the derivation of Lagrange's Identity. Apart from this the concept is not important.)

2. We shall now consider a special case. A system may be said to be stationary if the distribution of stellar positions and velocities is the same (approximately) at all times. "Distribution" is interpreted in the following sense. We imagine a lattice superposed on the 6-dimensional position-velocity space R^6 with the rectangular coordinates x, y, z, u, v, w. Every star of the system is represented by a point in R^6, whose coordinates coincide with the star's positional coordinates and velocity components. The system is therefore represented by a cloud of points in R^6 in respect of its spatial as well as its kinematic behaviour. The mesh size of the lattice is now chosen in such a way that there are many meshes at time $t = 0$ in which there are a large number of image points. Then, for every instant t, there is a well-defined number N of image points within or on the boundary of every mesh M. (A convention has, of course, to be found to decide the mesh to which each boundary belongs.) This assignation of the numbers N to the meshes M is called the distribution of the system at time t.

A stationary state implies a distribution which is (approximately) constant in time. For stationary systems it evidently follows that

$$T(t) \approx T(0) = \hat{T} = \text{const} \left.\right\}$$
$$U(t) \approx U(0) = \hat{U} = \text{const} \left.\right\}$$

so that, following the virial theorem,

$$T \approx -E, \ U \approx 2E,$$

and therefore $\qquad 2T + U \approx 0.$

For the following applications of these relations we shall assume that the systems concerned are stationary or, at least, that the instantaneous values of the kinetic and potential energies are not substantially different from their time averages.

3. The virial theorem may be employed to improve considerably the estimates of mass, made in the previous paragraph, for systems which are approximately spherically symmetrical

Besides stability we must also assume a stationary state. We are therefore putting more conditions into the calculation, but obtain a more precise answer as a result.

According to the criterion of stability in § 3

$$E = T + U < 0,$$

if the system is stable. From this there follows a certain lower bound for the total mass M. But with the present conditions, the virial theorem leads to the relation

$$2T + U = 0.$$

Since T is linear and U quadratic in M, a comparison of the last two formulae immediately shows the following. The value of the mass deduced from the virial theorem equals exactly twice the lower bound deduced from Lagrange's Identity. Thus we derive, from the estimates of § 3.5, the new formula

$$M \approx 6\alpha \frac{r_* \overline{R^2}}{G}$$

$$\approx 1 \cdot 4 \times 10^3 \, \alpha r_* \, \overline{R^2} \, [\odot].$$

The orders of magnitude 10^6 and 10^{11} solar masses for globular clusters and galaxies, respectively, therefore remain.

4. One can estimate the total mass of our Galaxy in a similar way. We only indicate an outline of the method.

The following assumptions are made:

(a) The globular clusters move only under the influence of the force of gravitation exerted on them by the flattened "main body" of the Galactic System.

(b) The system as a whole is stationary.

(c) The total mass m of all the globular clusters is small in comparison with the mass M of the main body. (If we assume that the mass of the globular clusters is known, possibly in consequence of the investigation in Section 3, the assumption (c) is superfluous. It is required only if m has to be considered to be unknown and then serves to eliminate this quantity in comparison with M.)

F

We now apply the virial theorem. Let R be the measured radial velocity of a particular globular cluster with respect to the point occupied by the Sun at time $t = 0$ and let $\overline{R^2}$ be the mean square of R. Then the total kinetic energy of the assembly of all globular clusters is proportional to $m\overline{R^2}$. The stationary main body here serves as a reference system at rest. The inner potential energy of the assembly (its potential with respect to itself) is proportional to Gm^2/r_*, where r_* is the radius of the system of globular clusters. The potential energy of the assembly with respect to the main body is GmM/r_*. Owing to the assumption $m \ll M$ the inner potential energy is neglected, and we obtain the proportionality

$$M \sim \overline{R^2} r_*/G$$

from the virial theorem for M. More exact considerations only serve to estimate the numerical factor of proportionality. We represent the central body, for example, by a circular disk of uniform density. The numerical factor is then of order unity. Now

$$\sqrt{\overline{R^2}} \approx 100 \ [\text{km s}^{-1}], \ r_* \approx 10^4 \ [\text{pc}], \ G = \tfrac{1}{233},$$

and so
$$M \approx 2 \times 10^{11} \ [\odot],$$

which agrees with the order of magnitude found for the mean mass of the galaxies. What we have described here was really only an estimate of the order of magnitude. More accurate calculations may be found in the literature.

We have only been dealing with particle systems so far but have, none the less, employed the concept of a continuous (smooth) distribution of matter. This was done solely to estimate more conveniently the potential energy U of the system. The continuum model used here has no essential significance.

5. We conclude this section with an application of the virial theorem to a cosmogonical problem.

The opinion has occasionally been expressed (and it used to be the author's view) that the globular clusters, which are at present such strongly concentrated systems, were originally extended systems with little or no central concentration and no internal motions of any significance. In the course of time, it is said these systems contracted owing to their internal gravitation. We shall now explain why the hypothesis is untenable in this form.

At time $t = 0$, when the cluster of stars originated, the kinetic energy $T_{t=0}$ would have been approximately equal to zero, and the potential energy $U_{t=0}$ approximately equal to the total energy E, which must therefore be negative. Let us suppose that the virial theorem is applicable. For time $t = 0$ we define a mean distance $\bar{r}$ of the stars by

$$-\tfrac{1}{2}G\frac{M^2}{\bar{r}} = U_{t=0} = E.$$

Now the time average $\hat{U}$ of the potential energy is

$$\hat{U} = 2E.$$

A certain space and time-average $\tilde{r}$ of the stellar distances corresponds to this U, and is defined by

$$-\tfrac{1}{2}G\frac{M^2}{\tilde{r}} = \hat{U} = 2E.$$

We see at once that $\tilde{r} = \tfrac{1}{2}\bar{r},$

so that the time average of the mean distance of two stars is just half as large as their mean distance at the beginning of the evolution. The system is therefore not very much more concentrated now, on the average, than it was at the outset. Conditions of great concentration can only be very rarely met, or else the systems must pass through them very rapidly. But in either case one can hardly assume that we should see almost all these clusters in just this improbable condition. Our hypothesis concerning their original condition must therefore be dropped, or at least modified.

It seems, however, extremely doubtful whether one may assume a high initial concentration. The strongest argument against this is provided by two systems which have approximately spherical symmetry (in the constellations Fornax and Sculptor) and which correspond exactly, owing to their great extension and weak concentration, to the evolutionary hypothesis we have just rejected. Such structures could have developed from a different initial state only under some very special conditions.

If one wants to return to the above hypothesis one must assume that there are additional processes which can scatter energy, such as frictional forces exerted on the stars in their motion through interstellar material. However, hardly any trace of interstellar material has ever been found in globular clusters. Possibly it has been gradually absorbed by the stars. We shall stop here so as not to lose ourselves in speculation. In any case all these matters are as yet largely unexplained and can, apparently, not be cleared up at all by means of the mechanics of stellar systems alone.

5. Similarity transformations

1. In all applications of Lagrange's Identity and of the virial theorem we encounter expressions which are very similar to one another, as for instance GM/r. The coefficients of the expressions are, as a rule, of order unity. We shall now demonstrate that this is no coincidence.

We begin with Newton's equations of motion

$$m_i \ddot{x}_i = -\frac{\partial U}{\partial x_i}, \quad \text{etc.,}$$

$$U = -G \sum_{i<j} \frac{m_i m_j}{|\mathbf{r}_i - \mathbf{r}_j|},$$

and introduce the dimensionless variables $\tilde{t}$, $\tilde{x}_i$, $\tilde{y}_i$, $\tilde{z}_i$ and $\tilde{U}$, which are related to the corresponding dimensional variables by the equations

$$\left.\begin{aligned}
x_i &= x_* \tilde{x}_i, & t &= t_* \tilde{t}, \\
y_i &= x_* \tilde{y}_i, & U &= U_* \tilde{U}. \\
z_i &= x_* \tilde{z}_i,
\end{aligned}\right\}$$

t_*, x_* and U_* denote positive factors of proportionality with the appropriate dimensions. Further, let

$$\tilde{m}_i = m_i/M, \quad \text{where} \quad M = \sum_i^n m_i,$$

be dimensionless masses. Substitution of these expressions into the equations of motion gives

$$\frac{Mx_*}{t_*^2} \tilde{m}_i \frac{d^2\tilde{x}_i}{d\tilde{t}^2} = -\frac{U_*}{x_*} \frac{\partial \tilde{U}}{\partial \tilde{x}_i}, \quad \text{etc.,}$$

$$U_* \tilde{U} = -\frac{GM^2}{x_*} \sum_{i<j} \frac{\tilde{m}_i \tilde{m}_j}{|\tilde{\mathbf{r}}_i - \tilde{\mathbf{r}}_j|}.$$

We now choose the dimensional factors to be such that they cancel from all the equations by setting

$$\frac{M x_*}{t_*^2} = \frac{U_*}{x_*},$$

$$U_* = \frac{G M^2}{x_*},$$

from which it follows that

$$\frac{G M}{x_*} = \left(\frac{x_*}{t_*}\right)^2.$$

This is equivalent to

$$\frac{1}{2} \frac{G M^2}{x_*} = \tfrac{1}{2} M \left(\frac{x_*}{t_*}\right)^2,$$

or to

$$t_* = \frac{1}{\sqrt{\left(G \dfrac{M_*}{x_*^3}\right)}}.$$

The last three relations express the proportionality of certain characteristic dimensional quantities. The first refers to the proportionality of the potential and kinetic energies for a single particle, the second the proportionality of these energies for the whole system, and the third defines a natural time scale for the system. As stated, all this applies only to the dimensional factors of these particular quantities. The quantities themselves differ from these factors by time-dependent numerical coefficients given by the solutions

$$\tilde{x}_i = \tilde{\psi}_i(\tilde{t}), \text{ etc.}$$

of the dimensionless equations of motion

$$\tilde{m}_i \frac{d^2 \tilde{x}_i}{d \tilde{t}^2} = -\frac{\partial \tilde{U}}{\partial \tilde{x}_i}, \quad \text{etc.},$$

$$\tilde{U} = -\sum_{i<j} \frac{\tilde{m}_i \tilde{m}_j}{|\tilde{r}_i - \tilde{r}_j|}.$$

Every solution of this set corresponds to a one-parameter family of solutions of the set of dimensional equations, namely

$$x_i = x_* \tilde{\psi}_i(\tilde{t})$$

$$= x_* \tilde{\psi}_i(t/t_*)$$

$$= x_* \tilde{\psi}_i \left\{ t \Big/ \left(G \frac{M}{x_*^3}\right) \right\}, \quad \text{etc.}$$

The configurations belonging to different solutions of the family are, and remain, geometrically similar to one another, provided the time variable is also subjected to a suitable transformation of scale, and the corresponding instants are chosen correctly for the comparison between the different configurations. Corresponding instants are such that they all belong to the same value $\tilde{t}$.

The values of the masses m_i have been assumed to remain fixed in the transformations. But dimensional relations can also be set up for a comparison of systems with different masses. The number of particles in all the systems must then be the same, and the masses of corresponding particles proportional. This happens, for example, when (with a given number of particles) all the masses are equal in each one of the systems under comparison. When the masses are varied, the family of solutions of the dimensional equations

$$x_i = x_* \tilde{\psi}_i \left\{ t \Big/ \left(G \frac{M}{x_*^3} \right) \right\}.$$

belonging to a single dimensionless solution $\tilde{\psi}_i(\tilde{t})$, evidently depends on two parameters such as, for example, the characteristic length x_* and the total mass M.

We have not yet given an exact significance to the characteristic length x_*. Let us choose for x_* the radius of the system (if this exists), or the average distance of all pairs of stars, or some such similar quantity. We then obtain the relation

$$t_* \approx \frac{1}{\sqrt{(G\bar{\rho})}}$$

for the time scale of the system, where $\bar{\rho}$ denotes its mean density. It is now clear why the factors of proportionality derived from Lagrange's Identity and the virial theorem must be of order unity. For, following § 1.3, the potential energy $U(r_*)$ of a sphere of radius r_* may be calculated by means of the formulae

$$\frac{\mathrm{d}}{\mathrm{d}r}\left(r^2 \frac{\mathrm{d}V}{\mathrm{d}r} \right) = 4\pi G r^2 \rho(r)$$

and
$$\frac{\mathrm{d}U}{\mathrm{d}r} = - V(r)\, \rho(r)\, 4\pi r^2.$$

On introducing the dimensionless variables we find that

$$V(r_*) = \frac{GM}{r_*}.\,\text{const},$$

and

$$U(r_*) = -\frac{GM^2}{r_*}.\,\text{const}.$$

Both numerical factors can be calculated by integrations, over the interval $0 \ldots 1$, of dimensionless functions, whose average order of magnitude is unity. (This follows at once from the corresponding dimensionless equations for $\tilde{V}(\tilde{r})$ and $\tilde{U}(\tilde{r})$.) The integrals, and also the factors of proportionality, are then of order unity as well.

It can similarly be seen that a star requires an interval of time of order t_* to move along a path of the chosen length x_*, if its initial velocity was zero.

The structure of the previous formulae can now be readily understood, and we have obtained two further results. We have shown that there exists a one (or two) parameter family of dimensional solutions and that there is a natural (dynamical) scale of time.

2. We now ask whether there are systems which permanently remain similar to themselves. To answer this question we must express the conditions of similarity in terms of formulae, and introduce them into the general equations of motion. This method yields necessary conditions for the possible solutions. If these can be satisfied at all, it still remains to be seen whether the corresponding configurations really do represent the initial conditions for solutions, or, rather, what additional conditions the system must satisfy to remain similar to its initial configuration for all times.

The similarity condition may be written

$$\boldsymbol{r}_i(t) = s(t)\,\mathbf{A}(t).\,\overset{\circ}{\boldsymbol{r}}_i, \qquad i = 1, 2, \ldots, n.$$

Here $s(t)$ denotes the time-dependent scale factor, $\mathbf{A}(t)$ the rotation matrix and $\overset{\circ}{\boldsymbol{r}}_i$ the fixed initial position vectors of n particles with respect to their centre of mass. Then

$$\overset{\circ}{\boldsymbol{r}}_i = \boldsymbol{r}_i(0)$$

so that $\qquad\qquad s(0) = 1 \quad$ and $\quad \mathbf{A}(0) = \mathbf{I},$

the unit matrix.

We now introduce the similarity conditions into the equations of motion

$$m_i \ddot{\boldsymbol{r}}_i = \boldsymbol{k}_i.$$

On differentiating $\boldsymbol{r}_i(t)$ twice with respect to t, we obtain

$$\ddot{\boldsymbol{r}}_i = (\ddot{s}\mathbf{A} + 2\dot{s}\dot{\mathbf{A}} + s\ddot{\mathbf{A}}) \cdot \overset{\circ}{\boldsymbol{r}}_i.$$

The gravitational forces $\boldsymbol{k}_i$ alter in that they are subject to the same rotation as the position vectors and a multiplication by the factor s^{-2}, so that

$$\boldsymbol{k}_i = \frac{1}{s^2} \mathbf{A} \cdot \overset{\circ}{\boldsymbol{k}}_i,$$

where $\overset{\circ}{\boldsymbol{k}}_i$ denotes the force on the ith particle at time $t = 0$.

Insertion of these formulae into the equations of motion yields

$$m_i(\ddot{s}\mathbf{A} + 2\dot{s}\dot{\mathbf{A}} + s\ddot{\mathbf{A}}) \cdot \overset{\circ}{\boldsymbol{r}}_i = \frac{1}{s^2} \mathbf{A} \cdot \overset{\circ}{\boldsymbol{k}}_i,$$

and on pre-multiplication by $\mathbf{A}^{-1}$ we find

$$m_i[\ddot{s}\mathbf{I} + 2\dot{s}\boldsymbol{\Omega} + s(\dot{\boldsymbol{\Omega}} + \boldsymbol{\Omega}^2)] \cdot \overset{\circ}{\boldsymbol{r}}_i = \frac{1}{s^2} \overset{\circ}{\boldsymbol{k}}_i.$$

We have introduced the notation

$$\boldsymbol{\Omega} = \mathbf{A}^{-1} \cdot \dot{\mathbf{A}}$$

and taken account of the relation

$$\mathbf{A}^{-1} \cdot \ddot{\mathbf{A}} = \dot{\boldsymbol{\Omega}} + \boldsymbol{\Omega}^2,$$

which follows from it.

Two cases may now be distinguished—depending on whether there are, in the initial configuration, three linearly independent position vectors or only two; depending, in other words, on whether the initial configuration is three-dimensional or plane. We shall not consider linear initial configurations.

3. In the three-dimensional case we can write down the transformed equations of motion for three linearly independent vectors $\overset{\circ}{\boldsymbol{r}}_1$, $\overset{\circ}{\boldsymbol{r}}_2$ and $\overset{\circ}{\boldsymbol{r}}_3$, and solve the resulting system of nine

equations for the nine unknown coefficients of the matrix in the square brackets. We find

$$s^2[\ddot{s}\mathbf{I} + 2\dot{s}\mathbf{\Omega} + s(\dot{\mathbf{\Omega}} + \mathbf{\Omega}^2)] = \mathbf{L},$$

where $\mathbf{L}$ is a time-independent matrix in which we are interested no further. Now $\mathbf{A}(t)$ has three independent elements and so has $\mathbf{\Omega}$. We therefore have a system of nine equations for four functions, that is for $s(t)$ and the three elements of $\mathbf{\Omega}$, and it is by no means self-evident that the equations are compatible. A necessary condition for self-consistency is $\mathbf{\Omega} \equiv 0$, so that $\dot{\mathbf{A}}(t) \equiv 0$ and $\mathbf{A}(t) \equiv \mathbf{I}$. There can therefore be no rotation. (Details of the elementary but lengthy proof of this may be found in the literature. We omit it here because we shall only make very limited use of systems of this type.) The equations of motion then read

$$m_i \ddot{s}\overset{\circ}{\boldsymbol{r}}_i = \frac{1}{s^2}\overset{\circ}{\boldsymbol{k}}_i.$$

The initial forces are therefore collinear with the initial position vectors. They are related to the vectors $m_i \overset{\circ}{\boldsymbol{r}}_i$ by a factor of proportionality which is the same for all the particles (and equals $\ddot{s}(0)$ in fact). Such configurations are said to be central.

It follows that all particles must move on fixed straight lines through the centre of mass, and they must behave as if each were attracted towards a fixed particle at the centre according to the Newtonian law of gravitation. The mass of this particle generally does not equal the total mass of the system. This can be seen from the equations of motion, written in the form

$$m_i \ddot{\boldsymbol{r}}_i = \frac{1}{s^2}\overset{\circ}{\boldsymbol{k}}_i = \frac{1}{s^2}m_i \ddot{s}(0)\,\overset{\circ}{\boldsymbol{r}}_i[s(0)]^2,$$

or

$$m_i \ddot{\boldsymbol{r}}_i = m_i \frac{\ddot{s}(0)\,|\overset{\circ}{\boldsymbol{r}}_i|^3}{|\boldsymbol{r}_i|^2}\frac{\boldsymbol{r}_i}{|\boldsymbol{r}_i|}.$$

The mass accelerating the ith particle is therefore proportional to the volume of a sphere whose centre is at the centre of gravity of the system and which has the initial position of the ith particle on its surface.

We can use these necessary conditions, for configurations which remain similar to themselves at all times, to enumerate the configurations themselves completely. The particles are arranged, at time $t = 0$, in a three-dimensional central configuration and given initial velocities $\dot{s}(0)\, \overset{\circ}{\boldsymbol{r}}_i$, where $\dot{s}(0)$ is an arbitrary constant. Then, and only then, will the configuration of the n particles be similar at all times to the initial configuration.

An explicit description does not appear to have been given yet of all the possible central configurations for given masses $m_1, \ldots, m_n$, particularly in the three-dimensional case. The problem is certainly simplified if all the masses are assumed to be equal. In that case one can easily think up arrangements with spherical symmetry which lead to central configurations.

4. We still have to deal with the case of a plane initial configuration, and begin once again from the equations of motion

$$m_i[\ddot{s}\mathbf{I} + 2\dot{s}\boldsymbol{\Omega} + s(\dot{\boldsymbol{\Omega}} + \boldsymbol{\Omega}^2)]\, \overset{\circ}{\boldsymbol{r}}_i = \frac{1}{s^2}\, \overset{\circ}{\boldsymbol{k}}_i.$$

Let the (x, y) plane contain the initial configuration, so that all $\overset{\circ}{z}_i$ vanish. Then the z-components of every initial force is also evidently zero. Now write down the equations of motion for two linearly independent vectors $\overset{\circ}{\boldsymbol{r}}_1$ and $\overset{\circ}{\boldsymbol{r}}_2$, and consider the resulting set of six equations in the four unknown functions, namely the scale factor s and the three coefficients of $\boldsymbol{\Omega}$. It is found that the only possible rotation is about the z-axis. The plane of the configuration remains the same at all times, and the matrix $\boldsymbol{\Omega}$ has at most one element ω which differs from zero, and which corresponds to the angular velocity about the z-axis. The following relation connects the angular velocity $\omega = \omega(t)$ with the scale factor $s = s(t)$:

$$\ddot{s} - \omega^2 s = \frac{\text{const}}{s^2}.$$

The principle of conservation of angular momentum (III, § 1.3) can now be used. The similarity conditions are introduced and account is taken of the particular type of rotation possible. The principle takes the special form

$$\omega s^2 = \text{const},$$

or, in differential form,

$$\frac{d}{dt}(\omega s^2) \equiv 0.$$

In order to clarify the meaning of the two equations

$$\left.\begin{aligned}\ddot{s} - \omega^2 s &= \frac{\text{const}}{s^2}, \\[1em] \frac{d}{dt}(\omega s^2) &= 0,\end{aligned}\right\}$$

we may consider the motion of an imaginary particle, of mass unity, say, in the (ξ_1, ξ_2)-plane under the influence of a Newtonian force of gravitation towards the origin of coordinates. Let the equations of motion

$$\ddot{\xi}_i = -\frac{\text{const}}{s^2}\frac{\xi_i}{s}, \quad s = |\sqrt{(\xi_1^2 + \xi_2^2)}|, \quad \text{const} > 0$$

be transformed to polar coordinates s, θ, and let ω denote the angular velocity $\dot{\theta}$. This leads exactly to the two equations above, which are therefore equations of motion in polar coordinates.

With these results it follows from the equations of motion that the initial forces $\mathring{k}_i$ satisfy

$$\mathring{k}_i = m_i(\ddot{s} - \omega^2 s)\,\mathring{r}_i,$$

so that the initial configuration must be central. By means of the equation for $\ddot{s}$ we have, further, that

$$\mathring{k}_i = m_i.\text{const}.\mathring{r}_i.$$

Now
$$k_i = \frac{1}{s^2}\mathbf{A}.\mathring{k}_i \quad \text{and} \quad r_i = s\mathbf{A}.\mathring{r}_i,$$

so that finally
$$k_i = m_i\frac{\text{const}}{s^2}\mathbf{A}.\mathring{r}_i$$

$$= m_i\frac{\text{const}}{s^2}\frac{r_i}{s}$$

$$= m_i\frac{\text{const}\,|\mathring{r}_i|^3}{|r_i|^2}\frac{r_i}{|r_i|}.$$

The configuration of the n particles is consequently central at every instant, every particle is subject at all times to a Newtonian attraction towards the mass centre, and the attracting mass is proportional to the volume of a sphere about the mass centre, with the initial position of the ith particle on its surface. This all corresponds to the three-dimensional case.

As in that case, all the actual solutions of the problem can be found from the necessary conditions. It follows from

$$r_i = s\mathbf{A} \cdot \mathring{r}_i,$$

or

$$\dot{r}_i = \dot{s}\mathbf{A} \cdot \mathring{r}_i + s\dot{\mathbf{A}} \cdot \mathring{r}_i,$$

that the particles of a central configuration must be given the initial velocities

$$\dot{r}_i(0) = \dot{s}(0)\,\mathring{r}_i + \dot{\mathbf{A}} \cdot \mathring{r}_i,$$

where $\dot{s}(0)$ and $\dot{\mathbf{A}}(0)$ are arbitrary constant number and matrix, respectively. If $\dot{\mathbf{A}}(0) = 0$, we obtain linear motions of the same type as in the case of a three-dimensional initial configuration. While these were the only motions possible then, we can, in the present case, superpose rotations $\dot{\mathbf{A}}(0) \neq 0$. All particles therefore describe similar conic sections, which may become circles if $\dot{s}(0) = 0$.

5. Similarity solutions are significant because they are the only ones which can be explicitly calculated. In the case of three-dimensional initial configurations they provide (very rough) models for non-stationary stellar systems with spherical symmetry; in the case of plane initial configurations they are models of strongly flattened stellar systems in rotation, which may or may not be stationary.

Of course there probably are different initial conditions in real stellar systems. If they differ only relatively little from those in the ideal models, then the latter are likely to be useful approximations for the duration of the time scale t_*, which we introduced in § 5.1. For, according to III, § 2.1, the solutions of a set of differential equations depend continuously on the initial conditions. Two solutions belonging to neighbouring initial conditions may then be expected to differ by only a small amount for an interval corresponding to unit dimensionless length, or a time t_*.

However, only in very rare cases will the initial conditions in real stellar systems actually approximate to central configurations. For in the three-dimensional case the condition is that, for a given particle, the effective gravitating mass attracting it to the zero point shall be proportional to the volume of the sphere through the initial position of the particle. The "mass density" must be uniform as a result, at least in the case of spherical symmetry, and this happens only rarely in globular clusters or galaxies. In the plane case the rotation is forced to occur with the same angular velocity for all the stars. But we should expect, by analogy with the planetary system, that the outer stars have smaller angular velocities than the inner ones; the available observations (I, § 5.1) confirm this view to some extent.

6. Perhaps the system of galaxies provides the most promising application for the similarity model. We must, however, postulate, in addition to the validity of Newtonian mechanics, that the system is finite and approximately spherically symmetrical. It then seems very likely that its mass distribution approximates to that in a central configuration. The further necessary condition for the system to remain similar to itself is fulfilled. For this stated that the velocity of the ith particle at time $t = 0$ shall be given by

$$\dot{\boldsymbol{r}}_i(0) = \dot{s}(0)\,\overset{\scriptscriptstyle 0}{\boldsymbol{r}}_i.$$

According to I, § 5.3, observation shows that

$$(\dot{\boldsymbol{r}}_i - \dot{\boldsymbol{r}}_1)_{t=0} = K(\boldsymbol{r}_i - \boldsymbol{r}_1)_{t=0},$$

where $\boldsymbol{r}_1$ denotes the position vector of our Galaxy. Without significant loss of generality we may assume that there is a galaxy which remains at the centre of the whole system of galaxies for all time. If its position vector is set equal to zero in the empirical equation it follows, first of all, that

$$\dot{\boldsymbol{r}}_1(0) = K\overset{\scriptscriptstyle 0}{\boldsymbol{r}}_1,$$

and from this that

$$\dot{\boldsymbol{r}}_i(0) = K\overset{\scriptscriptstyle 0}{\boldsymbol{r}}_i, \quad \text{for all} \quad i = 1, 2, ..., n.$$

This is the additional necessary and sufficient condition for similarity. (It remains valid for all times t, if it holds for $t = 0$.

For
$$\boldsymbol{r}_i(t) = s(t)\,\boldsymbol{\mathring{r}}_i \quad \text{and} \quad \boldsymbol{\dot{r}}_i(t) = \dot{s}(t)\,\boldsymbol{\mathring{r}}_i$$

imply
$$\boldsymbol{\dot{r}}_i(t) = \frac{\dot{s}(t)}{s(t)}\,\boldsymbol{r}_i(t),$$

for all t.)

The types of motion of the model are fully known. Because we have

$$\ddot{s} = -\frac{\text{const}}{s^2} = \frac{\ddot{s}(0)}{s^2},$$

we can regard $s(t)$ as the coordinate of a particle moving along a straight line under the influence of a fixed Newtonian centre of attraction at the origin. This is a Keplerian motion along a straight line. The total energy of the fictitious particle is

$$E = \tfrac{1}{2}\dot{s}^2 + \frac{\ddot{s}(0)}{s}$$

$$= \tfrac{1}{2}\{\dot{s}(0)\}^2 + \frac{\ddot{s}(0)}{s(0)}$$

$$= \tfrac{1}{2}K^2 + \ddot{s}(0).$$

Depending on whether this is negative or not, the particle oscillates within fixed limits on the axis, or $s(t) \to \infty$ for $t \to \pm\infty$. In a corresponding way, the model for the system of galaxies either oscillates, or else it initially contracts from infinity to a single point ($s = 0$) and then expands to infinity again. In either case there is a singularity when $s = 0$, which does not necessarily exist in reality, since the true initial conditions need only approximate to a central configuration.

We now assume that this model is applicable to the system of galaxies and shall try to find the sign of the quantity E which decides the nature of the motion. For this we require an empirical value for $\ddot{s}(0)$, which we derive as follows:

From the equation of motion

$$m_i \ddot{s}\boldsymbol{\mathring{r}}_i = \frac{1}{s^2}\,\boldsymbol{\mathring{k}}_i$$

of § 5.3 we deduce that, for $t = 0$,

$$m_i \ddot{s}(0)\,\boldsymbol{\mathring{r}}_i = \boldsymbol{\mathring{k}}_i.$$

The value of $\mathring{k}_i$ can be estimated, as in §§ 3 and 4, by means of a fictitious continuous distribution of matter with spherical symmetry. Let ρ be the constant mass density; we then have Poisson's equation

$$\frac{1}{r^2}\frac{d}{dr}\left(r^2\frac{dV}{dr}\right) = 4\pi G\rho.$$

(V, as usual, denotes the gravitational potential referred to a unit mass, and r the radial distance.) We deduce that

$$\frac{dV}{dr} = \frac{4\pi}{3}G\rho r.$$

Now the force $\mathring{k}_i$ is (approximately) equal to the product of the negative gradient of the potential and the mass, so that

$$\mathring{k}_i = -m_i\left(\frac{dV}{dr}\right)_{r=|\mathring{r}_i|}\cdot\frac{\mathring{r}_i}{|\mathring{r}_i|}$$

$$= -\frac{4\pi}{3}Gm_i\rho\mathring{r}_i.$$

We insert this into the equation for $\ddot{s}(0)$ to find that

$$\ddot{s}(0) = -\frac{4\pi}{3}G\rho$$

and therefore
$$E = \tfrac{1}{2}K^2 - \frac{4\pi}{3}G\rho.$$

Now ρ equals the number of galaxies per unit volume multiplied by the average mass of a galaxy. From the data of I, § 5.3,

$$\rho \approx 5 \times 10^{-18} \times 10^{11} = 5 \times 10^{-7}\ [\odot\ \mathrm{pc}^{-3}].$$

Further
$$K \approx 1 \times 10^{-4}\ [Z^{-1}],$$

also according to I, § 5.3, and

$$G = \tfrac{1}{233}.$$

Thus it follows that

$$E \approx 5 \times 10^{-9} - 8 \times 10^{-9} < 0.$$

The corresponding Keplerian motion along the straight line is of the elliptical kind and the motion of the system is periodic.

Since $\dddot{s}(0)$ is determined, all the details of the motion may be calculated in an elementary way; in particular the instant t_1 of the singularity can be found. We shall not perform the calculation but merely estimate t_1. The order of magnitude of $(-t_1)$ is that of the time-scale

$$t_* = \frac{1}{\sqrt{(G\rho)}},$$

or 2×10^{10} years in round figures.

The observational data are rather inexact so that all these numerical estimates are unreliable. We cannot even be certain of the sign of E, which determines the nature of the evolution in the large.

6. Mechanically open systems

1. We have, so far, considered stellar systems as mechanically closed structures, and have treated them as such. This implies that we have assumed all the forces acting on a system to be *internal*, in other words to be forces between pairs of particles of the system. We shall drop the assumption in this paragraph (and only here). We are prompted to do so by the existence of open star clusters, which are probably not mechanically closed, but interact markedly with the stellar fields around them.

Let the equations of motion for the n stars of such a cluster be

$$m_i \ddot{r}_i = k_i, \qquad i = 1, 2, \ldots, n.$$

Each force k_i is a resultant of two subsidiary forces, one due to the other stars of the cluster, and the other due to the whole Galactic System. We shall denote the first component by $m_i F(r_i)$, and the second by $m_i f(r_i)$.

The motion of the mass centre r_* of the cluster is determined by

$$M\ddot{r}_* = \sum_1^n k_i, \qquad M = \sum_1^n m_i,$$

according to III, § 1.2, and because all the internal forces add up to zero in the sum of all the forces, by the relation

$$M\ddot{r}_* = \sum_1^n m_i f(r_i).$$

We now assume the dimensions of the system to be so small that the vectors $f(r_i)$ can be approximated sufficiently closely by the linear expressions

$$f(r_i) = f(r_*) + \mathbf{L}(r_*) \cdot (r_i - r_*).$$

$\mathbf{L}(r_*)$ here denotes the matrix of the partial derivatives, with respect to x, y and z, of the components of $f(r)$. We then have, for the mass centre, that

$$M\ddot{r}_* = Mf(r_*) + \mathbf{L}(r_*) \sum_1^n m_i(r_i - r_*),$$

or
$$\ddot{r}_* = f(r_*).$$

The motion of an individual star relative to the mass centre is determined by

$$(r_i - r_*)^{\cdot\cdot} = F(r_i) + f(r_i) - f(r_*)$$
$$= F(r_i) + \mathbf{L}(r_*) \cdot (r_i - r_*).$$

We shall say that a cluster is stable if the external forces do not disintegrate it. This is a new meaning of the word, different from that in § 3. If there is stability, all the forces must act inwards at all times. (We shall shortly justify this statement.) The forces
$$F(r_i) + \mathbf{L}(r_*) \cdot (r_i - r_*)$$

must therefore be such that their components along the direction from r_* to r_i always act towards the mass centre r_*, and must therefore always be negative. Conversely, this is evidently a sufficient condition for stability.

It might have been thought that, to ensure stability, the forces need not necessarily act in an inward direction at all times, and that it might be sufficient if the forces were occasionally positive, and then negative for a long enough time to make the stars stay close together. But it must be remembered that the more a cluster has dissolved, the weaker is its internal gravitation, which alone ensures its continued existence. Even if the stability depends, in addition, on the external force it seems permissible to assume, in general, that there is no means of arresting the dissolution, once it has begun, and that the sign of the resultant force remains positive, once it has become positive.

G

In order to derive, from these conditions, a necessary criterion which is simple in application, we now introduce the additional assumption that the cluster is approximately spherically symmetrical. We denote the magnitude of the "field intensity" $\boldsymbol{f(r)}$ by $f(\boldsymbol{r})$, and the derivative of $f(\boldsymbol{r})$, in the direction of $\boldsymbol{f(r)}$, by $f'(\boldsymbol{r})$. Let the particle with suffix 1 be on the edge of the system, and let it be such that the direction of $(\boldsymbol{r}_1 - \boldsymbol{r}_*)$ coincides with that of $\boldsymbol{f(r_*)}$. If the system is stable, then

$$-G\frac{M}{\bar{r}^2} + f'(\boldsymbol{r}_*) \mid \boldsymbol{r}_1 - \boldsymbol{r}_* \mid < 0,$$

where $\bar{r}$ denotes the radius of the system, so that

$$\frac{GM}{\bar{r}^3} > f'(\boldsymbol{r}_*)$$

for every point $\boldsymbol{r}_*$ occupied by the mass centre and for every value $\bar{r}$ taken by the radius in the course of time.

2. An estimate of $f'(\boldsymbol{r}_*)$, admittedly a very rough one, may be made by assuming that the whole mass μ of the Galactic System is concentrated at its centre. If the centre of the cluster being considered is at a distance $\mathscr{D}$ from the Galactic centre, then

$$f(\mathscr{D}) = -\frac{G\mu}{\mathscr{D}^2}$$

and

$$f'(\mathscr{D}) = \frac{2G\mu}{\mathscr{D}^3}$$

(the meaning of f and f' having been altered slightly). The criterion becomes

$$\frac{M}{\bar{r}^3} > 2\frac{\mu}{\mathscr{D}^3}.$$

If the cluster is stable, its mean density must be at least twice as large as that of a sphere about the Galactic centre, having the centre of the cluster on its surface, and being uniformly filled with the total mass of the Galaxy.

With the data

$$\mu = 2 \times 10^{11} \, [\odot], \quad \mathscr{D} = 10^4 \, [\text{pc}] \quad \text{or} \quad \mathscr{D} = 5 \times 10^3 \, [\text{pc}],$$

for example, we find that, for stability,

$$\bar\rho > \tfrac{1}{10} \quad \text{or} \quad \bar\rho > \sim 1 \qquad [\odot \; \mathrm{pc}^{-3}],$$

respectively. This estimate is not very reliable, as we have pointed out, because the gradient of the force at any point is strongly affected by the local distribution of mass (cf. the general Poisson's equation). Our assumed field of force is probably too much idealized.

3. We now estimate the time scale t_* of the cluster, with this last proviso. We use the method of § 5.1 to introduce, into the equations of motion, a set of dimensionless variables with fixed dimensional factors of proportionality. If, in addition, we write

$$\sigma = \frac{\mu}{(4\pi/3)\mathscr{D}^3},$$

we find that

$$t_* = \frac{1}{\sqrt{(G \,|\, 2\sigma - \bar\rho \,|)}}.$$

This result can be understood as follows. The exterior forces act as if the mean density $\bar\rho$ had been diminished by 2σ. This was already made plausible by the form of the criterion of stability.

If the cluster is stable, t_* gives the order of magnitude of the time required by a star to traverse the cluster. If the cluster is unstable, t_* is a measure of the time required for its dissolution. This time therefore depends on the position of the cluster—as one would have expected in any case.

7. Summary

It was the main purpose of this chapter to give a description, in the large, of the types of motion followed by systems of gravitating particles. Hopf's theorems were fundamental to our task. The first of these states that there are, effectively, only two such types of motion: recurrence or disintegration. According to the second theorem, the types of motion are "almost always" the same for both past and future. The theorems apply to all systems in which the forces depend only on the positions of the particles, and are free of singularities. To remove the singularities of the Newtonian forces of gravitation we changed the law of force in a suitable way for small distances (§ 1 and 2).

The next problem was to decide between the two types of motion in an arbitrarily given stellar system. This led to the enunciation of Lagrange's Identity, and to its application as Jacobi's criterion of stability. According to this, a system having positive total energy disintegrates. If it has zero energy, it will usually disintegrate, and if it has negative total energy the criterion gives no information (§ 3).

However, if we know a system to be stable, the virial theorem can be deduced from Lagrange's Identity. It states that both the kinetic and the potential energies have time averages, which are simple multiples of the total energy. The virial theorem, as well as Lagrange's Identity, can be used to estimate the masses of real stellar systems (§ 3 and 4).

In applications we repeatedly found expressions of a certain type. Their structure was explained by means of the introduction of dimensionless variables. At the same time we saw that, to every single type of motion, there corresponds a one or two parameter family of "mechanically similar" types of motion. The family is formed from the given type by a simultaneous change in the scales of length and time, as well as the total mass in the two parameter case. The discussion also showed the existence of a natural time scale for every system, inversely proportional to the square root of its mean density (§ 5).

These similarity transformations led us to investigate those systems which remain similar to themselves with the passage of time. It was found that the initial configurations of such systems must be central, and that there were two principal cases to be considered. In the case of a three-dimensional initial configuration, the only type of motion possible is an expansion or a contraction; in the case of a plane initial configuration, a rotation may be superposed on this. In both cases each particle moves as though it were under the influence of a Newtonian attraction towards the mass centre; the effective attracting mass depends on the initial position of the particle (§ 5).

Only in exceptional cases can an application of these models be made to real stellar systems. Nevertheless, the models may be considered to represent the simplest types of spherical and rotating stellar systems, respectively. The three-dimensional model can be applied to the system of galaxies. Here the observational data are not precise enough to determine uniquely the type of motion. The time which has elapsed since the system passed through its state of greatest concentration is of the order of the time scale, i.e. 10^9 or 10^{10} years (§ 5).

Finally we investigated mechanically open systems, in particular open clusters, to determine their stability with respect to external disturbing forces. The limit of stability is, evidently, related to a certain degree of compactness of the system. The calculation yielded a critical mean density for the cluster below which it cannot resist the external forces tending to dissolve it. These estimates are, however, not very reliable (§ 6).

This ends our study of stellar systems from the point of view of celestial mechanics.

Examples

1. Use the following argument to make plausible the validity of Poisson's equation. Suppose that the potential (defined in its integral form) is to be differentiated at the point r. Enclose this point in a sphere of very small radius, decompose the integral expression into the two corresponding sums, take the density ρ to be constant within the small sphere, and then perform the calculation. This, of course, only shows the plausibility of the theorem, but does not prove it.

2. Transform Poisson's equation from Cartesian to polar and to cylindrical coordinates, and then specialize it to apply to distributions of mass with either spherical or rotational symmetry.

3. Prove the theorems of § 1.3 concerning the gravitating spherical shell.

4. Determine the factor of proportionality in the formula of § 4.4 for the mass of the Galactic System.

5. How can one construct central configurations with spherical symmetry when all the particles have equal masses (§ 5.3)?

Comments and References to the Literature

§ 1.2. Much effort has been spent on investigations of collisions in systems of gravitating particles. See

[15] WINTNER, A., *The Analytical Foundations of Celestial Mechanics*, Princeton, 1941.

However, in the opinion of the author, it is hard to feel that this problem has any scientific significance, or much interest mathematically. The way out in the present text seems both natural and simple.

Wintner's book is distinguished from all the other books known to me by its mathematical rigour and by its exposition of the inwardness of the subject. It omits useless calculations, which are inessential for a true understanding and may even hinder it, and its historical and biblio graphical comments are exceptionally instructive.

§ **1.3.** An almost ideal textbook dealing with potential theory is that of
[16] KELLOGG, O. D., *Foundations of Potential Theory*, Berlin, 1929.

§ **2.2.** It is curious that Hopf's theorems are still not well known although they are of fundamental significance in mechanics. Cf.:
[17] HOPF, E., Zwei Sätze über den wahrscheinlichen Verlauf der Bewegungen dynamischer Systeme, *Math. Ann.*, **103**, 710, 1930

§ **3.2.** A criterion of stability, due to G. F. Hil'mi, may be mentioned here. The author knows it only from a review by W. Kaplan.
[18] HIL'MI, G. F., On completely unstable systems of n gravitating bodies, *Doklady Akad. Nauk. SSSR.* (N.S.), **79**, 419–422, 1951. (In Russian.)
[19] KAPLAN, W., *Mathematical Reviews*, **13**, 789, 1952.

Kaplan writes: "In the classical n-body problem, let r_{ij} denote the distance between particles p_i and p_j at time t, let

$$q(t) = \min (r_{ij}), \quad s(t) = \min (\dot{r}_{ij}), \quad m_i = \text{mass of } p_i,$$

$$M' = \Sigma\, m_i m_j, \quad M'' = \min \frac{m_i m_j}{m_i + m_j}, \quad M = M'/M''.$$

Units are chosen so that the constant of gravitation is 1. It is then proved that if $s(0) > 0$ and $s^2(0)\, q(0) > 8M$, then $q(t) \to \infty$ as $t \to \infty$".

This is, admittedly, rather a weak criterion, since M has the order of magnitude of $n^2 m_i$.

§ **3.3.** In some investigations a "velocity of escape" v_∞ is calculated and used. It is defined as the speed required, by a star on the edge of the spherical system, to make its total energy zero instantaneously. Thus

$$\tfrac{1}{2} v_\infty^2 - \frac{GM}{r_*} = 0.$$

It is then usually assumed that a star with this or with a higher energy will actually leave the system. The problem is thus simply reduced to that of two bodies. It is doubtful whether this procedure is reliable. The motion of the star in the course of time also depends, for example, on its initial direction and, to a large extent, on the motions of the remaining stars. It is certainly safe to suppose that a particle will escape to infinity if it is remote enough from the system and is moving away from it at a high enough speed. The same is true if the star is inside the system and has an exceptionally high speed. We consider the concept of an escape velocity to have a meaning only under the following two conditions. (a) There is a high probability of the star's escaping only at speeds considerably larger than that given in the formula; (b) The lower limit to these speeds is always indefinite.

§ **4.3.** We put $\alpha = 1$. The formula in the text gives, then,

$$2\overline{v^2} = \frac{GM}{r_*},$$

and, in connexion with the previous remark,

$$(\overline{v^2})^{\frac{1}{2}} = \tfrac{1}{2}v_\infty.$$

The formula is occasionally applied, but we consider it to have little significance.

In an earlier work the author determined the masses of globular clusters by using the virial theorem in a different way. Since then Schwarzschild and Bernstein have criticized that method of estimating the potential energy and the author considers their remarks to be, in essence, justified. From his present point of view he considers the formula given in Chapter V, § 4.5, to be the best available.

[20] KURTH, R., *Z. Astrophysik*, **29**, 26, 1951.

[21] SCHWARZSCHILD, M., and BERNSTEIN, S., Note on the mass of M92, *Astrophys. J.*, **122**, 200, 1955.

§ **4.4.** An estimate of the factor of proportionality may be found in an article by the author:

[22] KURTH, R., Die Masse des Milchstrassensystems, *Z. Astrophysik*, **28**, 60, 1950.

§ **4.5.** The contractional hypothesis has recently been treated in particular by:

[23] VON DER PAHLEN, E., Ueber die Entstehung sphärischer Sternsysteme, *Z. Astrophysik*, **24**, 68, 1947.

The author supported these views in:

[24] KURTH, R., Die Entwicklung der Kugelsternhaufen, *Z. Astrophysik*, **29**, 33, 1951.

But, as the text shows, he has changed his opinion, and now holds that the contractional hypothesis demands the assumed existence of dissipative forces. The opposing "hypothesis of evacuation" ("Verödungshypothese") is certainly no better founded. The arguments adduced in its support from statistical mechanics are not sound, and it is contradicted by the existence of the systems in the constellations Sculptor and Fornax. These, being only weakly concentrated, are hard to distinguish from the general field of stars, and difficult to discover. It is therefore by no means impossible that there are more systems of this kind, which are as yet unknown.

By means of the method of § 3.1, a generalized Lagrange's Identity may be constructed even in the presence of a resisting medium, provided the frictional forces are proportional to the velocities of the stars. The motion of the system must become rather strange after a sufficient length of time, when the friction has destroyed a large amount of mechanical energy. It is easily shown, and it is also self-evident, that there are no time averages. On the other hand, Liouville's theorem can be used (in its general form, i.e. for the time derivative of the functional determinant). One finds that if M is the image, at time t, of the set $\overset{\circ}{M}$ of initial points in the $6n$-dimensional phase space, then the measure of M tends to zero as $t \to \infty$. But M cannot contract to a point, for then time averages would exist. It is also clear from the equations of motion themselves that they have no time-independent solutions. In reality the stars will fall into one another.

§ **4.** In an application of the virial theorem, due to Jeans, the following statement appears to be proved: If several systems, originally distinct, unite to form a common system, the dimensions of the latter are of larger order of magnitude than the distances between the original single systems. For comparison, see also:

> [25] VON DER PAHLEN, E., *Einführung in die Dynamik von Stern-systemen*, Basel, 1947.

However, the argument is seen to be false if the right energies are assumed for the single systems, and if their interactions are taken into account.

Among the advantages of Pahlen's book are its clear structure, its readability, reasonable size and wide outlook. Lindblad's presentation of the theory may also be recommended:

> [26] LINDBLAD, B., "Die Milchstrasse", in *Handbuch der Astrophysik*, Berlin, 1933.

§ **5.3.** For the missing proofs, see Wintner [15]. They refer only to the necessary conditions. It seems superfluous to establish in detail the sufficiency of the conditions we have given.

For large n the central initial configuration in three dimensions can be represented by a uniform and continuous distribution of mass with spherical symmetry. Cf. v. d. Pahlen [23], where this is also generalized. The same types of motion are then found by a simple method, which is easily grasped, if less rigorous.

§ **5.4.** For the necessary conditions, see Wintner [15] once more.

§ **5.6.** The finiteness of the system is to be interpreted in its widest sense. In the case of a (continuous) structure with spherical symmetry it is enough if there is a large nucleus of uniform density, surrounded by an envelope with an arbitrary density distribution. Since the latter exerts no force on the nucleus, the types of motion we have derived will continue in the innermost parts of the nucleus until the elements of mass from the envelope penetrate there.

It is, further, very remarkable that there should be so little numerical difference between the two terms contained in the expression for E. (This is why uncertainties in their values carry so much weight.) Let us assume, for example, that $E = 0$ is the true value. It follows from the equation of energy that

$$\tfrac{1}{2}\dot{s}^2 - \frac{4\pi}{3}\frac{G\rho}{s} = 0,$$

$$\sqrt{s}\,ds = \frac{8\pi}{3}\,G\rho\,dt,$$

and

$$s = (6\pi G\rho)^{\frac{1}{3}}(t-t_1)^{\frac{2}{3}},$$

$$t_1 = -(6\pi G\rho)^{\frac{1}{2}} \approx -5 \times 10^9 \text{ [years]}.$$

The assumption $E = 0$ would have the following significance cosmogonically. A very long time ago $(t \to -\infty)$ the system, dispersed and at rest, began to contract under the influence of its own gravitation. It reached its greatest density at time t_1, and has been expanding since then. It is, of course, very uncertain whether the model is applicable for such a long interval of time. For, first of all, the initial configuration was only approximately central at best. Secondly, the physical evolution of the system must be considered. The indications are that its present physical state is about 10^9 years of age. Thirdly, the mechanical and physical development of the system cannot be followed with any certainty through the instant t_1 of the greatest concentration. On the other hand, the play of our ideas—for that is all it was—makes the statement $E \approx 0$ comprehensible, while it would remain unexplained otherwise.

§ **6.1.** It is tacitly assumed, as a rule, that the external field of force acts on the system in the same way at all times. This is not generally the case, since the cluster moves in the external field.

§ **6.2, 6.3.** The model of a cluster is often specialized in that its density is assumed to be uniform and constant. One is then not content with an estimate of, say, the time scale, but calculates everything explicitly, which is possible with these assumptions and with them only. In spite of the greater effort expended on calculation, the method leads to no further results, particularly to none which are more reliable, for the assumption of constant density is a complete idealization.

Chandrasekhar has made more exact calculations based on the assumption of an ellipsoidal structure. See:

[27] CHANDRASEKHAR, S., *The Principles of Stellar Dynamics*, Chicago, 1947.

The assumption of constant density is also made in this book, so that no benefit is derived from the more exact treatment of the shape of the systems.

Chandrasekhar's book is exceptionally clear in its structure and its development of ideas. It concentrates more on the formal part of the theory.

CHAPTER V

STELLAR SYSTEMS AS GRAVITATING CONTINUA

1. General remarks

1. We have had occasion, in previous chapters, to represent real stellar systems by continuous mass distributions rather than by sets of particles. This was done, however, only for the sake of simplifying the calculations, and did not change our fundamental model of a system of discrete particles. In contrast, the basic model of the present chapter is a continuous distribution of gravitating matter. The mass of the stars is no longer represented as being concentrated into points; on the contrary it is pictured as being "smeared out" between the stars.

This new model is suggested by the fact that there are a large number of stars in a system. It permits and, in fact, demands a very much more complete consideration of the shape and structure of stellar systems than was possible with particle mechanics. The spherical, ellipsoidal or spiral shape of a stellar system can now be treated much better than before. The new model does not have the hindersome superfluous accuracy of particle mechanics, whose criteria were suitable for predicting even the behaviour of individual stars; as was the case, for example, with Jacobi's criterion of stability.

On the other hand the evolution of a system is, in the long run, doubtless influenced to a large extent by the "grainy" structure of its material. The interactions of neighbouring stars will make themselves felt during long intervals of time, but they are explicitly neglected in the continuum hypothesis.

The continuum model will therefore describe a real stellar system for a limited period of time only. The extent to which the two basic hypotheses are useful can be defined as follows: The particle model is applicable to problems concerning the evolution in the large, while the continuum model is of more use for shorter time intervals. Of course we still have to decide the meaning of the terms "short" and "long".

2. It would be possible simply to imagine a smearing out of the material in real space. This would be equivalent to a hydro-dynamical hypothesis, but would give a bad approximation to reality. The velocity of the moving material would become, at any instant, a single-valued function of position. (The function would also have to be continuous to make any theory feasible.) But observation shows that there can often be great differences, in speed and direction of motion, between stars which are close neighbours in space and are therefore described by neighbouring "elements of material". To take account of this the material must be considered to be spread out, not only in the three-dimensional space Γ_x, but in the six-dimensional position-velocity space Γ, which we may also call the phase space of the system. The meaning of the term "phase space" differs in what follows from that in Chapter IV.

We define the concept more closely as follows. Let x_1, x_2 and x_3 be orthogonal Cartesian coordinates in real space Γ_x, and let u_1, u_2 and u_3 be the corresponding velocity components. The position vectors (x_1, x_2, x_3) will be briefly denoted by x, and the velocity vectors (u_1, u_2, u_3) by u. The assembly of all u will be called the velocity space Γ_u of the system, whose phase space Γ is the Cartesian product $\Gamma_x \times \Gamma_u$.

As in IV, § 4.2, the position x and the velocity u of a single star will be represented together by the point (u, x) in phase space Γ. At every instant the system is described by a cloud of points in Γ which, in general, changes with time.

We shall describe the distribution of material in Γ by means of a material density $f(u, x, t)$, which is called the frequency function of the system. By definition it is non-negative. The integral

$$\iiint_G \iiint f(u, x, t)\, du_1\, du_2\, du_3\, dx_1\, dx_2\, dx_3$$

over any sub-region G of Γ shall equal the total mass of all the stars whose image points in Γ are within G. This integral will from now on be abbreviated to

$$\iint_G f(u, x, t)\, du\, dx.$$

Corresponding abbreviations will be made for other integrals.

The conditions we have just imposed can, of course, not be strictly fulfilled, for the integral is a continuous function of the set G, while the total mass is discontinuous. The frequency function can thus only yield an approximate description of the stellar system. This inaccuracy seems to be unavoidable in principle. It is not only a defect of the model, but is a necessary consequence of our summary method of describing the system, which pays no attention to the behaviour of any one particular star. We can only hope to gain insight into the inner structure of the system by setting up such a description, but it is bought at the cost of accuracy.

The method of IV, § 4.2, can also be used to make an explicit determination of the frequency function for the given system. A lattice is superposed on phase space, and the value of the frequency function at the centre point of each mesh is defined to be the mean mass density in that mesh. The frequency function is defined at other points in Γ by the "smoothest possible" interpolation of values, but we shall not specify how this is to be done. We can, without loss of generality, assume the distribution function to be bounded and continuously differentiable in Γ.

3. The stars of a real system move under the influence of their mutual gravitation. In the continuum model we interpret this by means of a flow of the material substrate which fills the phase space Γ. Newton's law of motion (or rather its analogue) describes this flow in a differential form

$$\left.\begin{aligned} \dot{u}_i &= -V_i(x, t), \\ \dot{x}_i &= u_i. \end{aligned}\right\} \qquad i = 1, 2, 3.$$

Here
$$V_i \equiv \frac{\partial}{\partial x_i} V(x, t)$$

denotes the gradient of the gravitational potential $V(x, t)$, which is due to the whole substrate and refers to a unit mass.

We assume that the equations possess a "sensible" solution

$$\left.\begin{aligned} u_i &= \phi_i(\overset{0}{u}, \overset{0}{x}, t), \\ x_i &= \psi_i(\overset{0}{u}, \overset{0}{x}, t), \end{aligned}\right\} \qquad i = 1, 2, 3,$$

or all instants t and all points $(\mathring{u}, \mathring{x})$ in the space, and satisfy the nitial conditions

$$\left.\begin{array}{l} \phi_i(\mathring{u}, \mathring{x}, 0) = \mathring{u}_i, \\ \psi_i(\mathring{u}, \mathring{x}, 0) = \mathring{x}_i. \end{array}\right\} \quad i = 1, 2, 3.$$

The physical significance of the equations provides a justification for this assumption; the basis of a formal proof is sketched out in § 5.2.

Liouville's theorem of III, § 3.3, in its stricter form, applies to he solutions ϕ_i, ψ_i. For evidently

$$\sum_1^3 \left\{ \frac{\partial(-V_i)}{\partial u_i} + \frac{\partial u_i}{\partial x_i} \right\} \equiv 0,$$

o that the functional determinant (Jacobian)

$$\Delta(\mathring{u}, \mathring{x}, t) \equiv \begin{vmatrix} \dfrac{\partial \phi_1}{\partial \mathring{u}_1}, & \cdots, & \dfrac{\partial \phi_1}{\partial \mathring{x}_3} \\ \vdots & & \\ \dfrac{\partial \psi_3}{\partial \mathring{u}_1}, & \cdots, & \dfrac{\partial \psi_3}{\partial \mathring{x}_3} \end{vmatrix}$$

equals unity for all t and all $(\mathring{u}, \mathring{x})$.

4. Let now $\mathring{G}$ be any sub-region of Γ and, at time t, let its mage be G, the set of all points (u, x) which correspond to the points $(\mathring{u}, \mathring{x})$ of $\mathring{G}$ in the transformation

$$\left.\begin{array}{l} u_i = \phi_i(\mathring{u}, \mathring{x}, t), \\ x_i = \psi_i(\mathring{u}, \mathring{x}, t). \end{array}\right\}$$

The conservation of mass implies that

$$\iint_G f(u, x, t) \, du \, dx = \iint_{\mathring{G}} f(\mathring{u}, \mathring{x}, 0) \, d\mathring{u} \, d\mathring{x}.$$

Just as in III, § 3.4, we now transform the region of integration G, on the left-hand side, into $\mathring{G}$, and move everything on to one side, bearing in mind Liouville's theorem

$$\Delta(\mathring{u}, \mathring{x}, t) \equiv 1.$$

It follows that

$$\iint_{\mathring{G}} [f\{\phi(\mathring{u}, \mathring{x}, t), \psi(\mathring{u}, \mathring{x}, t), t\} - f(\mathring{u}, \mathring{x}, 0)]\, d\mathring{u}\, d\mathring{x} = 0,$$

for all $\mathring{G}$ and all t, and so

$$f(\phi, \psi, t) = f(\mathring{u}, \mathring{x}, 0),$$

for all $\mathring{u}$, $\mathring{x}$ and t. Thus the frequency function is an integral of the equations of motion. This theorem, which is fundamental for the whole theory, is usually named after Poincaré, Charlier or Jeans.

According to III, § 2.3, the theorem can also be cast into a differential form by differentiating the last equation with respect to the time variable t, transforming the independent variables $\mathring{u}, \mathring{x}, t$ into the independent variables u, x, t by means of the solution functions ϕ_i, ψ_i, and taking account of the equations of motion. In this way we find that a necessary condition to be satisfied by the frequency function is Liouville's equation

$$\frac{\partial f}{\partial t} - \frac{\partial f}{\partial u_j} V_j + \frac{\partial f}{\partial x_j} u_j = 0.$$

We here introduce the convention, to apply from now on, that terms with repeated suffixes are to be summed from 1 to 3.

2. Hydrodynamics

1. We suggested, in § 1.2, that conventional hydrodynamics cannot give a good description of stellar systems. We shall now set out more exactly how our hypothesis is related to hydrodynamics. We shall try to derive the hydrodynamical equations, or their analogues, from our basic assumptions—in so far as this is possible.

We adopt the following procedure. Liouville's equation is multiplied, in turn, by

$$1, u_j, u_j u_k, u_j u_k u_l, \ldots.$$

We then integrate over the velocity space Γ_u. After some elementary transformations, in particular after several partial integrations, we obtain equations for the expectation values of the quantities by which the equation was multiplied. The expectation values are calculated with the aid of the probability density

$$\frac{f(u, x, t)}{\int_{\Gamma_v} f(v, x, t)\, dv},$$

defined in the velocity space Γ_u. In the language of probability theory, this is the density of a conditional probability with the statistical variable u and parameters x and t. It is to be regarded as a statement of the probability distribution of u, while the values of x and t are to be considered as given.

If $g(u, x, t)$ is any function of u, x and t, its (conditional) expectation value $\bar{g} = \bar{g}(x, t)$ is defined by

$$\bar{g} = \frac{\int_{\Gamma_u} g(u, x, t) f(u, x, t)\, du}{\int_{\Gamma_u} f(u, x, t)\, du}.$$

This method leads directly to equations for the expectation values $\bar{u}_i$, $\overline{u_i u_j}$, ... The only exception is the first equation, which contains the term $\bar{I}$. It involves the function

$$\rho(x, t) = \int_{\Gamma_u} f(u, x, t)\, du,$$

which evidently represents the mass density of the model in position space Γ_x. The resulting equation,

$$\frac{\partial \rho}{\partial t} + \frac{\partial}{\partial x_i}(\rho \bar{u}_i) = 0,$$

is identical with the hydrodynamical equation of continuity.

For the mean velocity $\bar{u}_i$ we obtain a generalization of Euler's hydrodynamical equations

$$\frac{\partial \bar{u}_i}{\partial t} + \frac{\partial \bar{u}_i}{\partial x_j}\bar{u}_j = -V_i - \frac{1}{\rho}\frac{\partial}{\partial x_j}\{\rho \overline{(u_i - \bar{u}_i)(u_j - \bar{u}_j)}\}.$$

The generalization is that the "second order moment"

$$\overline{(u_i - \bar{u}_i)(u_j - \bar{u}_j)}$$

on the right side, which corresponds to the pressure in Euler's equations, is now a dyadic tensor and no longer a scalar, as it was there.

2. We shall now prove these statements by deriving the equations of hydrodynamics from Liouville's equation

$$\frac{\partial f}{\partial t} + \frac{\partial f}{\partial x_i} u_i - \frac{\partial f}{\partial u_i} V_i = 0.$$

On integration over velocity space Γ_u we find

$$\frac{\partial}{\partial t} \int_{\Gamma_u} f \, du + \frac{\partial}{\partial x_j} \int_{\Gamma_u} f u_j \, du - V_j \int_{\Gamma_u} \frac{\partial f}{\partial u_j} \, du = 0.$$

The frequency function can, without loss of generality, be assumed to vanish for large speeds $u = |\sqrt{(u_i u_i)}|$. Then

$$\int_{\Gamma_u} \frac{\partial f}{\partial u_1} \, du = \iint_{-a}^{a} \{ f(a, u_2, u_3) - f(-a, u_2, u_3) \} \, du_2 \, du_3 = 0,$$

if a denotes a sufficiently large positive number. We obtain

$$\frac{\partial \rho}{\partial t} + \frac{\partial}{\partial x_j} (\rho \bar{u}_j) = 0,$$

as stated.

Euler's equations are derived in a similar way. We have

$$\frac{\partial}{\partial t} \int_{\Gamma_u} f u_i \, du + \frac{\partial}{\partial x_j} \int_{\Gamma_u} f u_i u_j \, du - V_j \int_{\Gamma_u} \frac{\partial f}{\partial u_j} u_i \, du = 0,$$

or

$$\frac{\partial}{\partial t} (\rho \bar{u}_i) + \frac{\partial}{\partial x_j} (\rho \overline{u_i u_j}) - V_j \int_{\Gamma_u} \frac{\partial f}{\partial u_j} u_i \, du = 0.$$

We now transform the last term by writing

$$\frac{\partial f}{\partial u_j} u_i \equiv \frac{\partial}{\partial u_j} (f u_i) - f \delta_{ij},$$

where

$$\delta_{ij} = \begin{cases} 1, & \text{when } i = j, \\ 0, & \text{when } i \neq j, \end{cases}$$

and denotes the Kronecker delta. It then follows that

$$\int_{\Gamma_u} \frac{\partial f}{\partial u_j} u_i \, du = \int_{\Gamma_u} \frac{\partial}{\partial u_j} (f u_i) \, du - \delta_{ij} \int_{\Gamma_u} f \, du$$

$$= 0 \qquad\qquad - \delta_{ij} \rho.$$

Hence
$$\frac{\partial}{\partial t}(\rho\bar{u}_i) = -\rho V_i - \frac{\partial}{\partial x_j}(\rho\overline{u_iu_j}),$$

or
$$\frac{\partial\rho}{\partial t}\bar{u}_i + \rho\frac{\partial\bar{u}_i}{\partial t} = -\rho V_i - \frac{\partial\rho}{\partial x_j}\overline{u_iu_j} - \rho\frac{\partial}{\partial x_j}\overline{u_iu_j}.$$

The first term on the left is transformed, by means of the equation of continuity,

$$\frac{\partial\rho}{\partial t}\bar{u}_i = -\frac{\partial}{\partial x_j}(\rho\bar{u}_j)\,\bar{u}_i$$

$$= -\frac{\partial\rho}{\partial x_j}\bar{u}_i\bar{u}_j - \rho\frac{\partial\bar{u}_j}{\partial x_j}\bar{u}_i$$

$$= -\frac{\partial\rho}{\partial x_j}\bar{u}_i\bar{u}_j - \rho\left\{\frac{\partial}{\partial x_j}(\bar{u}_i\bar{u}_j) - \frac{\partial\bar{u}_i}{\partial x_j}\bar{u}_j\right\}.$$

On division by ρ, and with a rearrangement of terms, it now follows that

$$\frac{\partial\bar{u}_i}{\partial t} + \frac{\partial\bar{u}_i}{\partial x_j}\bar{u}_j = -V_i - \frac{1}{\rho}\left\{\frac{\partial\rho}{\partial x_j}(\overline{u_iu_j} - \bar{u}_i\bar{u}_j) + \rho\frac{\partial}{\partial x_j}(\overline{u_iu_j} - \bar{u}_i\bar{u}_j)\right\}$$

$$= -V_i - \frac{1}{\rho}\frac{\partial}{\partial x_j}\{\rho(\overline{u_iu_j} - \bar{u}_i\bar{u}_j)\},$$

or
$$\frac{\partial\bar{u}_i}{\partial t} + \frac{\partial\bar{u}_i}{\partial x_j}\bar{u}_j = -V_i - \frac{1}{\rho}\frac{\partial}{\partial x_j}\{\rho\overline{(u_i - \bar{u}_i)(u_j - \bar{u}_j)}\}.$$

This is the generalization of Euler's equation.

3. We have considered only the equations for the zeroth and first-order moments, or for ρ and $\bar{u}_i$. Equations for moments of higher order may be derived in a corresponding way. They have no analogy in conventional hydrodynamics, where they are replaced by an "equation of state" relating pressure and density, which, in its turn, does not correspond to any equation in stellar dynamics. Our equations show the relation between phenomenological and stellar dynamical hydrodynamics. They are only of limited use in a study of stellar systems, for the following reason. The equations for the first-order moments contain an expression involving moments of the second order, owing to the factor u_j in the term $(\partial f/\partial x_j)\,u_j$ of Liouville's equation. Correspondingly, the equations for the kth order moments contain at least one

H

$(k+1)^{\text{th}}$ order moment. However far one goes along the sequence of equations in the moments, there are always more unknowns than there are equations determining them. No progress can be made without some *ad hoc* hypothesis.

A good assumption seems to be the following. Let the initial distribution $\overset{\circ}{f}(u, x)$ be given at time $t = 0$. Calculate its second-order moments $\overline{(u_i - \bar{u}_i)(u_j - \bar{u}_j)}$ as functions of position, and introduce them, as approximations, into the generalized Euler's equations. Do the same for the potential gradient V_i. There are then four approximate relations available for the four functions $\rho(x, t), \bar{u}_i(x, t)$, from which the "macroscopic" development of the system can be deduced approximately for an interval of time which is not too large.

Another possibility is to assume the existence of a stress tensor $p\delta_{ij}$ with spherical symmetry (effectively a scalar pressure) and to assume p to be proportional to a power of the density, as is the practice in the theory of gases.

4. In a few cases different methods may be suitable. For example, let us consider the Galaxy as a stationary structure, which is approximately axially symmetrical and has the Sun in its central plane. Let us choose the 3-axis perpendicular to the Galactic plane, and adopt the following two hypotheses:

(a) $\bar{u}_3 \equiv 0$;

(b) $\overline{(u_i - \bar{u}_i)(u_3 - \bar{u}_3)} = \sigma_3^2 \delta_{i3}, \qquad \sigma_3 = \text{const} > 0.$

The third of Euler's equations then leads to the relation

$$0 = -\frac{\partial}{\partial x_3} V(x_3) - \frac{1}{\rho} \frac{\partial}{\partial x_3} (\rho \sigma_3^2).$$

(The variables x_1 and x_2 are kept fixed here and do not, therefore, appear.) It follows that

$$\rho(x_3) = \rho(0) \exp\left[-(1/\sigma_3^2) V(x_3)\right].$$

For reasons of symmetry, V will be an even function of x_3. To a first approximation,

$$V(x_3) = \tfrac{1}{2}\gamma x_3^2, \qquad \gamma = \text{const} > 0,$$

and further

$$\rho(x_3) = \rho(0) \exp\left[-\tfrac{1}{2}(\gamma/\sigma_3^2) x_3^2\right].$$

The value of γ is still unknown. But the dispersion σ_3 of the velocities varies with the spectral type, so that the validity of the formula may be tested with respect to its dependence on both x_3 and σ_3, and it appears to be confirmed by observations. We may further deduce the following. According to observational evidence it seems that spectral types with large masses correspond to small dispersions σ_3. The formula then predicts that the more massive stars should be more strongly concentrated towards the Galactic plane. This is confirmed by observations (see I, § 1.3), and shows that there is a relation between the two empirical results.

The cosmological model of IV, § 5.6, can be taken over from particle mechanics into hydrodynamics. The pressure must now be assumed to be negligibly small. However, as expected, nothing new can be learnt from the re-formulation of the previous basic assumptions, and so we shall not go into any details.

5. A purely kinematic treatment turns out to be more fruitful than the dynamic one. The mean motion of the material in the position space Γ_x is determined by the equations

$$\dot{x}_i = \bar{u}_i(x,t), \qquad i = 1, 2, 3.$$

Let us imagine that it corresponds to a real flow

$$x_i = \chi_i(\overset{0}{x}, t)$$

in Γ_x. Now consider the relative motion of two elements of mass which are at the neighbouring points x and x'. We have

$$(x'_i - x_i)^{\cdot} = (x'_i)^{\cdot} - \dot{x}_i$$

$$= \bar{u}_i(x', t) - \bar{u}_i(x, t)$$

$$= \frac{\partial}{\partial x_j} \bar{u}_i(x, t) (x'_j - x_j),$$

to the first order. We introduce polar coordinates (r, α, β), with their origin at x, so that

$$x'_i - x_i = r e_i, \qquad i = 1, 2, 3,$$

where
$$\left. \begin{array}{l} e_1 = \cos \beta \cos \alpha, \\ e_2 = \cos \beta \sin \alpha, \\ e_3 = \sin \beta. \end{array} \right\}$$

The relative velocity has the components

$$(x_i' - x_i)^{\cdot} = \dot{r}e_i + r\dot{e}_i.$$

In order to have a convenient representation for $\dot{e}_i$, we now define the two vectors e_i' and e_i'' by the relations

$$\left.\begin{aligned} e_i' \cos\beta &= \frac{\partial e_i}{\partial \alpha}, \\[2ex] e_i'' &= \frac{\partial e_i}{\partial \beta}. \end{aligned}\right\}$$

It is easily seen, by means of geometrical arguments, or by calculation, that e_i, e_i', and e_i'' form a normalized orthogonal triad so that

$$\left.\begin{aligned} e_i e_i = 1, \quad e_i e_i' = 0, \quad e_i e_i'' &= 0, \\ e_i' e_i' = 1, \quad e_i' e_i'' &= 0, \\ e_i'' e_i'' &= 1. \end{aligned}\right\}$$

We now use polar coordinates for the expressions on both sides of the equation giving the relative velocity $(x_i' - x_i)^{\cdot}$, and find

$$\dot{r}e_i + re_i' \cos\beta \, \dot{\alpha} + re_i'' \dot{\beta} = \frac{\partial \bar{u}_i}{\partial x_j} re_j.$$

Making, successively, scalar multiplications with the vectors e_i, e_i', e_i'', we find that

$$\left.\begin{aligned} \dot{r} &= r \frac{\partial \bar{u}_i}{\partial x_j} e_i e_j, \\[2ex] \cos\beta \, \dot{\alpha} &= \frac{\partial \bar{u}_i}{\partial x_j} e_i' e_j, \\[2ex] \dot{\beta} &= \frac{\partial \bar{u}_i}{\partial x_j} e_i'' e_j. \end{aligned}\right\}$$

These are the equations which we had intended to derive. They predict the radial velocities $\dot{r}$ and the angular velocities $\dot{\alpha}$ and $\dot{\beta}$ found by an observer who is on the particle which has the position x at time t, and who investigates the velocities, relative to himself, of neighbouring elements of mass.

Before applying these fundamental kinematic equations there are two points to note. First, it follows from

$$\frac{\partial \bar{u}_i}{\partial x_j} e_i e_j = \frac{\partial \bar{u}_j}{\partial x_i} e_j e_i$$

(interchange of the dummy suffixes) that the first equation may be written, more symmetrically,

$$\dot{r} = r \cdot \frac{1}{2}\left(\frac{\partial \bar{u}_i}{\partial x_j} + \frac{\partial \bar{u}_j}{\partial x_i}\right)e_i e_j.$$

We cannot do this with the other two equations. The second point is that there is, of course, no reason which limits us to the linear approximation in the difference velocity $\{\bar{u}(x',t) - \bar{u}(x,t)\}$. Terms of higher order may be added, as required. We shall, however, confine ourselves here to the most important case, that of the linear approximation.

6. The first of the fundamental kinematical equations

$$\dot{r} = r\,K_{ij}e_i e_j, \quad K_{ij} = \frac{1}{2}\left(\frac{\partial \bar{u}_i}{\partial x_j} + \frac{\partial \bar{u}_j}{\partial x_i}\right)$$

will now be applied to the system of galaxies. We shall assume, for this purpose, that the observable part of the system is restricted to a region around our Galaxy which is small enough to permit the use of the linear approximation. According to our formula, and also to observation (I, § 5.3), the average radial velocities of the galaxies in a given direction of observation e_i are then proportional to the distance. There is also a simple law for their dependence on the direction. Given a fixed r, the points $e_i/\sqrt{\{|\dot{r}(e)|\}}$ lie on a second-order surface. According to observation $\dot{r}(e)$ is positive for all directions. The surface is therefore an ellipsoid. A sphere seems to be compatible with observations. We may then write

$$K_{ij} = K\delta_{ij}.$$

The value $K \approx 10^{-4}\,[Z^{-1}]$ was used previously, in IV, § 5.6.

The density of the system will, to a first approximation, be uniform in the vicinity of our Galaxy. In this way our basic idea can readily explain the two most significant cosmological facts. But without further observational results we shall not be able to deduce much more from it. We are here dealing with an infinitesimal hypothesis, or an approximation valid for sufficiently small r, and so all our work applies, without change, even to a non-Euclidian metric, such as is used in general relativity. The observational evidence is thus compatible with almost every model. There is, as a result, no empirical means of deciding between the different models, at least for the present.

7. Our second application of the fundamental kinematical equations concerns the Galactic System. We consider the neighbourhood of the Sun, which is assumed to lie in the Galactic plane. The angular coordinates α and β will be identified with the galactic longitude and latitude, l and b, respectively. For the sake of simplicity our investigation will be restricted to the Galactic plane only, so that both x_3 and $\bar{u}_3$ vanish identically.

After some manipulation, the fundamental equation can be written in the form

$$\left.\begin{aligned} \dot{r} &= r\{K + A \sin 2(l - l_0)\}, \\ \dot{l} &= B + A \cos 2(l - l_0), \\ \dot{b} &= 0, \end{aligned}\right\}$$

where

$$\left.\begin{aligned} A \cos 2l_0 &= \frac{1}{2}\left(\frac{\partial \bar{u}_2}{\partial x_1} + \frac{\partial \bar{u}_1}{\partial x_2}\right), \\ A \sin 2l_0 &= \frac{1}{2}\left(\frac{\partial \bar{u}_2}{\partial x_2} - \frac{\partial \bar{u}_1}{\partial x_1}\right), \\ B &= \frac{1}{2}\left(\frac{\partial \bar{u}_2}{\partial x_1} - \frac{\partial \bar{u}_1}{\partial x_2}\right), \\ K &= \frac{1}{2}\left(\frac{\partial \bar{u}_1}{\partial x_1} + \frac{\partial \bar{u}_2}{\partial x_2}\right). \end{aligned}\right\}$$

The calculation is quite straightforward. The direction cosines are expressed in terms of $\cos l$ and $\sin l$

$$\left.\begin{aligned} e_1 &= \cos l, \quad e_1' = -\sin l, \\ e_2 &= \sin l, \quad e_2' = \cos l, \end{aligned}\right\}$$

and these functions in terms of $\cos 2l$ and $\sin 2l$ by

$$\left.\begin{aligned} \cos^2 l &= \tfrac{1}{2}(1 + \cos 2l), \\ \sin^2 l &= \tfrac{1}{2}(1 - \cos 2l), \\ \cos l \sin l &= \tfrac{1}{2}\sin 2l. \end{aligned}\right\}$$

There is no need to reproduce the working in detail.

So far we have dealt with an arbitrary flow in the $(1, 2)$-plane. Let us now consider a stationary circular flow

$$
\begin{aligned}
x_1 &= \mathscr{D} \cos (\omega t + \delta), \\
x_2 &= \mathscr{D} \sin (\omega t + \delta).
\end{aligned}
$$

Here $\mathscr{D}$ denotes the distance from the centre of the rotation, $\omega = \omega(\mathscr{D})$ the angular velocity and $\delta = \delta(\mathscr{D})$ a phase angle. We then have that

$$
\begin{aligned}
\dot{x}_1 &\equiv \bar{u}_1 = -\omega x_2, \\
\dot{x}_2 &\equiv \bar{u}_2 = \omega x_1.
\end{aligned}
$$

It follows that

$$
\begin{aligned}
\frac{\partial \bar{u}_1}{\partial x_1} &= -\frac{d\omega}{d\mathscr{D}} \frac{x_1}{\mathscr{D}} x_2, &
\frac{\partial \bar{u}_2}{\partial x_1} &= +\frac{d\omega}{d\mathscr{D}} \frac{x_1}{\mathscr{D}} x_1 + \omega, \\
\frac{\partial \bar{u}_1}{\partial x_2} &= -\frac{d\omega}{d\mathscr{D}} \frac{x_2}{\mathscr{D}} x_2 - \omega, &
\frac{\partial \bar{u}_2}{\partial x_2} &= +\frac{d\omega}{d\mathscr{D}} \frac{x_2}{\mathscr{D}} x_1,
\end{aligned}
$$

and, further, that

$$
\begin{aligned}
A \cos 2l_0 &= \frac{1}{2} \frac{d\omega}{d\mathscr{D}} \frac{x_1^2 - x_2^2}{\mathscr{D}}, \\
A \sin 2l_0 &= \frac{d\omega}{d\mathscr{D}} \frac{x_1 x_2}{\mathscr{D}}, \\
B &= \omega + \frac{1}{2} \frac{d\omega}{d\mathscr{D}} \mathscr{D}, \\
K &= 0.
\end{aligned}
$$

Hence

$$
A = \pm \frac{1}{2} \frac{d\omega}{d\mathscr{D}} \mathscr{D},
$$

and therefore

$$
\begin{aligned}
\cos 2l_0 &= \pm \frac{x_1^2 - x_2^2}{\mathscr{D}^2}, \\
\sin 2l_0 &= \pm \frac{2x_1 x_2}{\mathscr{D}^2}.
\end{aligned}
$$

Now for the Sun

$$
\begin{aligned}
x_1 &= \mathscr{D} \cos l_\odot = -\mathscr{D} \cos l_C, \\
x_2 &= \mathscr{D} \sin l_\odot = -\mathscr{D} \sin l_C,
\end{aligned}
$$

where $l_\odot$ denotes the longitude of the Sun relative to the Galactic centre, and

$$l_C = l_\odot + 180°$$

the longitude of the Galactic centre relative to the Sun. Hence

$$\left.\begin{aligned}
\cos 2l_0 &= \pm (\cos^2 l_C - \sin^2 l_C) = \pm \cos 2l_C, \\
\sin 2l_0 &= \pm 2 \cos l_C \sin l_C = \pm \sin 2l_C, \\
2l_0 &= 2l_C + \begin{cases} 0° \\ 360° \end{cases} \quad \text{or} \quad 2l_0 = 2l_C \pm 180°.
\end{aligned}\right\}$$

We choose the first value for $2l_0$. The choice is arbitrary, since the various possibilities are only formally different ways of representing the same flow. The basic formulae for the relative motion are

$$\left.\begin{aligned}
\frac{\dot{r}}{r} &= A \sin 2(l - l_C), \\
\dot{l} &= B + A \cos 2(l - l_C).
\end{aligned}\right\}$$

They almost coincide with the empirical result of I, § 3.4. The divisor r was missing then, because the stars considered had a range of distances, over which an average was taken. It is still an open question whether the relatively few B and O stars, for which K is observationally found to differ from zero, really do move along orbits considerably distinct from circles. Possibly the line displacement in their spectra is due to some other physical cause, which simulates the effect of an additional radial velocity.

The formulae for the coefficients A and B can be written more symmetrically. For this purpose the scalar linear velocity

$$u = \omega \mathcal{D}$$

is introduced. It then follows from

$$\frac{du}{d\mathcal{D}} = \frac{d\omega}{d\mathcal{D}} \mathcal{D} + \omega,$$

from

$$A = \frac{1}{2} \frac{d\omega}{d\mathcal{D}} \mathcal{D}$$

and from

$$B = A + \omega,$$

that

$$A = \frac{1}{2}\left(\frac{du}{d\mathcal{D}} - \frac{u}{\mathcal{D}}\right), \quad B = \frac{1}{2}\left(\frac{du}{d\mathcal{D}} + \frac{u}{\mathcal{D}}\right),$$

or

$$\frac{u}{\mathcal{D}} = B - A, \quad \frac{du}{d\mathcal{D}} = B + A.$$

A and B are called Oort's constants. Their observed values are

$$A \approx +0{\cdot}018\,[Z^{-1}], \quad B \approx -0{\cdot}013\,[Z^{-1}].$$

The angular velocity

$$\omega = u/\mathscr{D}$$

is therefore

$$\omega = -0{\cdot}031\,[Z^{-1}],$$

and the period of revolution

$$T = \frac{2\pi}{|\omega|}$$

is consequently

$$T \approx 2 \times 10^2\,[Z] = 2 \times 10^8\,[\text{years}].$$

The negative value of ω shows that the rotation is in the sense of decreasing galactic longitude. With

$$\mathscr{D} \approx 9 \times 10^3\,[\text{pc}]$$

the linear velocity becomes

$$u \approx -2{\cdot}8 \times 10^2\,[\text{km/s}],$$

approximately in agreement with the value of about 200 [km/s], which was deduced from the radial velocities of the globular clusters, and was quoted in I, § 3.1.

The derivative of the rotational velocity u in the radial direction is

$$\frac{\mathrm{d}u}{\mathrm{d}\mathscr{D}} = +0{\cdot}005\,[Z^{-1}].$$

The rotational speed appears to increase outwards. We must, however, bear in mind that u is negative. A positive value of $\mathrm{d}u/\mathrm{d}\mathscr{D}$ thus implies a decrease of $|u|$ in the outward direction. The Sun is near the edge of the Galaxy so that this decrease was to be expected, from an analogy with the Planetary System. Of course, one has to be careful in drawing such conclusions—for a comparison see § 3.3.

The Galaxy will rotate with approximately constant angular velocity—i.e. like a rigid body—in the vicinity of its centre, provided that $\omega(0) \neq 0$, as we shall assume. Thus $|u|$ increases directly as $\mathscr{D}$, when $\mathscr{D}$ is small. Observation shows that $|u|$ decreases again later, and this is also made plausible by our analogy. The simplest curve of $|u|$ against $\mathscr{D}$ satisfying these conditions is sketched in Fig. 3, p. 11, and we now know the reason why it has this shape. By contrast, it has not yet been possible to interpret the corresponding curve for the Andromeda Nebula.

8. We shall now use the methods developed in the last section to improve the criterion (of IV, § 6, 1.2) for the stability of open star clusters. This stated that, in the case of stability,

$$G\bar{\rho} > \frac{1}{4\pi/3} f'(\boldsymbol{r}_*),$$

where $\bar{\rho}$ denotes the mean density of the cluster, $\boldsymbol{r}_*$ its centre point, and $f'(\boldsymbol{r}_*)$ the derivative of the magnitude of the field intensity along its direction of action.

Two assumptions are made. The first is that the direction of the field coincides, at points in the Galactic plane, with the direction towards the Galactic centre. The second is that the centripetal acceleration $u^2/\mathscr{D}$ is equal to the intensity of the field, so that

$$f(\mathscr{D}) = u^2/\mathscr{D}.$$

It follows on differentiation that

$$f'(\boldsymbol{r}_*) = -\frac{\mathrm{d}}{\mathrm{d}\mathscr{D}} f(\mathscr{D}) = -2\frac{u}{\mathscr{D}}\frac{\mathrm{d}u}{\mathrm{d}\mathscr{D}} + \frac{u^2}{\mathscr{D}^2}.$$

We express $u/\mathscr{D}$ and $\mathrm{d}u/\mathrm{d}\mathscr{D}$ in terms of A and B, and obtain the criterion

$$G\bar{\rho} > \frac{1}{4\pi/3} f'(\boldsymbol{r}_*) = \frac{1}{4\pi/3}(A-B)(3A+B).$$

With our assumed data this implies that

$$\bar{\rho} > \tfrac{1}{10}[\odot\ \mathrm{pc}^{-3}]$$

is a necessary condition of stability. The estimate seems more reliable than that of IV, § 6.2, since it is based only on local values of the field intensity. About the same value of the lower bound is found for the vicinity of the Sun.

9. We can, finally, make a simple estimate of the total Galactic mass μ, supposed concentrated in a point at its centre. From

$$\frac{G\mu}{\mathscr{D}^2} = \frac{u^2}{\mathscr{D}} = (A-B)^2 \mathscr{D}$$

it follows that

$$\mu = \frac{1}{G}(A-B)^2 \mathscr{D}^3$$

$$\approx 2 \times 10^{11} \, [\odot].$$

This agrees, in order of magnitude, with the values which we have quoted previously.

The estimate can be improved to some extent, for we have made use of only the one equation

$$f(\mathscr{D}) = \frac{u^2}{\mathscr{D}} = (A-B)^2 \mathscr{D}.$$

But, according to the previous section, there is a second equation available, namely

$$\frac{\mathrm{d}}{\mathrm{d}\mathscr{D}}f(\mathscr{D}) = \frac{\mathrm{d}}{\mathrm{d}\mathscr{D}}\left(\frac{u^2}{\mathscr{D}}\right) = -(A-B)(3A+B).$$

The field intensity can, therefore, be made to depend on two parameters, to be determined by means of the two equations. We may assume, for example, that the gravitational forces are due to the attraction of the central particle and, in addition, to that of the homogeneous ellipsoid of revolution which gives the best possible representation of the general shape of the Galaxy. Then

$$f(\mathscr{D}) = G\mu_1/\mathscr{D}^2 + G\zeta\mathscr{D},$$

where μ_1 denotes the mass of the central particle, and ζ is a constant with the dimensions of a density. In the case of a strongly flattened ellipsoid of revolution

$$\zeta \approx \frac{\mu_2}{(4\pi/3)a^3}.$$

Here μ_2 is the mass and a the major semi-axis of the ellipsoid. The derivation of the formula may be found in the literature.

The derivative $df/d\mathscr{D}$ is then given by

$$\frac{df}{d\mathscr{D}} = -2\frac{G\mu_1}{\mathscr{D}^3} + G\zeta,$$

and the two unknown quantities $G\mu_1/\mathscr{D}^3$ and $G\zeta$ by the two linear equations

$$\left.\begin{array}{l} \dfrac{G\mu_1}{\mathscr{D}^3} + G\zeta = (A-B)^2 \\[3mm] -2\dfrac{G\mu_1}{\mathscr{D}^3} + G\zeta = -(A-B)(3A+B). \end{array}\right\}$$

Their solution is $\dfrac{G\mu_1}{\mathscr{D}^3} = \tfrac{4}{3}A(A-B),$

$$G\zeta = -\tfrac{1}{3}(A-B)(A+3B),$$

and the ratio of the two components

$$G\zeta\mathscr{D} : \frac{G\mu_1}{\mathscr{D}^2} = G\zeta : \frac{G\mu_1}{\mathscr{D}^3}$$

$$= -\frac{A+3B}{4A}$$

$$\approx \tfrac{1}{9}.$$

The mass at the central point is by far the more important. We find the approximate values $1\cdot2 \times 10^{11}$ [$\odot$] and $0\cdot2 \times 10^{11}$ [$\odot$] for μ_1 and μ_2, respectively, when a is taken equal to about $1\cdot5 \times 10^4$ [pc]. The total mass is about $1\cdot4 \times 10^{11}$ [$\odot$], in agreement with our earlier estimates. The ellipsoid has the mean density $\mu_2/(4\pi/3)a^2c$, where c is the minor semi-axis. With $c \approx 3 \times 10^3$ [pc], its value is approximately 2×10^{-2} [$\odot$ pc^{-3}]. The Sun should, consequently, be in a region whose density (10^{-1} [$\odot$ pc^{-3}]) is greater than the average. While all these estimates are rather crude, there seem to be, in fact, empirical indications that the Sun is in the neighbourhood of a local density maximum. In this connexion one sometimes speaks of a "local stellar system". Nevertheless, the problem has not been completely settled, by any means.

Let us now consider the limitations of these methods. We have equated the field intensity with the centripetal acceleration. This holds for elements of material which move along circular orbits, but neither the stars themselves nor the elements of the continuum model do so (with relatively few exceptions). The velocity vector of the circular flow is an average, possibly variable in space and time, of the vectors which describe the actual motions. The field intensity $f(\mathcal{D})$ and the centripetal acceleration $u^2/\mathcal{D}$ will then be only approximately, but not exactly, equal. The difference may be important, particularly in the case of the derivatives. Our results are therefore good at most to an order of magnitude.

3. Application of the fundamental theorem

1. The observed streaming motions in the Galaxy have been explained satisfactorily by the kinematic theory of the previous paragraph. But the nature of the velocity distribution cannot be explained at all in this way. To do so we require the concept of a frequency function, which was explicitly eliminated in our hydromechanical treatment.

We now use this concept to define that of a velocity surface, introduced provisionally in I, § 3.3. Let $f(u, x, t)$ be the frequency function of a system, and let x and t be kept fixed. The surfaces

$$f(u, x, t) = \text{const}$$

in velocity space Γ_u are then called the velocity surfaces of the system at time t at the point x.

Observation shows that Schwarzschild's law

$$f(u, \mathring{x}, 0) = \text{const.} \exp\left[a_{ij}(u_i - \bar{u}_i)(u_j - \bar{u}_j)\right]$$

is approximately valid for the stars in the neighbourhood of the Sun. Here $\mathring{x}$ denotes the solar position, and the matrix (a_{ij}) is positive definite, so that the velocity surfaces are ellipsoids. This is plausible: the velocity surfaces will be closed, and it is also likely that they will be convex. The innermost surfaces must then be approximately ellipsoidal, since a quadratic polynomial is a good enough approximation to $f(u, \mathring{x}, 0)$ for them, and surfaces extending to infinity are excluded.

One will naturally assume that a law of Schwarzschild's type is valid, not only in the solar vicinity and at the present time but everywhere in the Galaxy and at all times (provided there has been no significant physical change in the state of the system) We shall try, in what follows, to explain this generalized Schwarzschild's law by means of the basic ideas of the continuum model and some additional hypotheses.

2. Our model of the Galaxy is based on these two assumptions: (a) The model is stationary, and (b) it has rotational symmetry, in the sense that the gravitational potential V is function of the two cylindrical coordinates

$$\mathscr{D} = |\sqrt{(x_1^2 + x_2^2)}| \quad \text{and} \quad z = x_3$$

only, so that $\qquad V = V(\mathscr{D}, z).$

According to the fundamental theorem of § 1.4, the frequency function f of the model is an integral of the equations of motion

$$\left.\begin{aligned}
\ddot{x}_1 &= -\frac{\partial V}{\partial x_1} = -\frac{\partial V}{\partial \mathscr{D}}\frac{x_1}{\mathscr{D}}, \\
\ddot{x}_2 &= -\frac{\partial V}{\partial x_2} = -\frac{\partial V}{\partial \mathscr{D}}\frac{x_2}{\mathscr{D}}, \\
\ddot{x}_3 &= -\frac{\partial V}{\partial x_3} = -\frac{\partial V}{\partial z}.
\end{aligned}\right\}$$

According to III, § 2.2, every function of the integrals is also an integral. For a general formulation of Schwarzschild's law an integral Q has to be found which is a positive definite quadratic form in the velocity components u_i. We can then write

$$f = \text{const.} \exp[-h^2 Q],$$

where h is a positive constant. This does not tell us why the exponential of Q, and not any other function, should be chosen. The real reason for the choice has never been clearly explained yet (cf. VI, § 3).

According to III, § 1.4, one known integral of the equations of motion is
$$E \equiv \tfrac{1}{2}u_j u_j + V(\mathscr{D}, z)$$
$$= \tfrac{1}{2}(\Pi^2 + \Theta^2 + Z^2) + V(\mathscr{D}, z),$$

the energy integral. Here $\mathscr{D}$, θ and z denote cylindrical coordinates, and Π, Θ and Z the corresponding linear velocity components. The velocity surface belonging to the energy integral is a sphere; it is therefore not sufficient, by itself, for a representation of Q and f. We need at least a second integral for that purpose.

The further integral follows without difficulty from the equations of motion. The vector $(\ddot{x}_1, \ddot{x}_2, 0) \equiv (x_1, x_2, 0)^{\cdot\cdot}$ is collinear with $(x_1, x_2, 0)$, and so

$$(x_1, x_2, 0)^{\cdot\cdot} \times (x_1, x_2, 0) = 0.$$

On integration with respect to the time we find that

$$(x_1, x_2, 0)^{\cdot} \times (x_1, x_2, 0) = \text{const.}$$

This implies that the vector $(0, 0, F_3)$, with

$$F_3 \equiv u_2 x_1 - u_1 x_2,$$

is constant with time. The function F_3 is an integral of the equations of motion. We shall call it the area integral, since F_3 is twice the rate at which the radius vector $(x_1, x_2, 0)$ sweeps out area in the $(1, 2)$ plane. F_3 is the angular momentum integral for a one-body system. In cylindrical coordinates it is expressed by

$$F_3 = \mathscr{D}\Theta,$$

as is easily verified and seems, indeed, evident.

3. To obtain an ellipsoidal velocity surface we now write

$$Q = 2E - 2k_1 F_3 + k_2 F_3^2,$$

where k_1 and k_2 are arbitrary constants. When explicit expressions are substituted for E and F_3 we find

$$Q = \Pi^2 + Z^2 + \lambda(\Theta - \Theta_0)^2 + 2V(\mathscr{D}, Z) - \frac{k_1^2 \mathscr{D}^2}{\lambda},$$

where
$$\lambda = 1 + k_2 \mathscr{D}^2$$

and
$$\Theta_0 = \frac{k_1 \mathscr{D}}{1 + k_2 \mathscr{D}^2}.$$

When $k_2 < 0$, the frequency function $f = f(Q)$ is positive only in an interval of $\mathscr{D}$ which is so small that $1 + k_2 \mathscr{D}^2 > 0$ at all its

points. Otherwise (that is if λ could be negative) there would b
velocity ellipsoids and hyperboloids.

The distribution function is even in Π, Z and $(\Theta - \Theta_0)$. Thes
three quantities all have the expectation value zero, so that

$$\overline{\Pi} = 0, \quad \overline{Z} = 0 \quad \text{and} \quad \overline{\Theta} = \Theta_0.$$

The mean motion is a circular flow, with the law of velocity

$$\overline{\Theta} = \frac{k_1 \mathscr{D}}{1 + k_2 \mathscr{D}^2},$$

in qualitative agreement with observational evidence from th
system $M33$ (cf. I, § 5.1). In particular

$$\left. \begin{array}{ll} \overline{\Theta} \sim \mathscr{D}, & \text{as } \mathscr{D} \to 0, \quad \text{provided } k_1 \neq 0, \\[2mm] \overline{\Theta} \sim 1/\mathscr{D}, & \text{as } \mathscr{D} \to \infty, \quad \text{provided } k_1 k_2 \neq 0. \end{array} \right\}$$

The first of these asymptotic relations shows that there i
approximately, rigid rotation near the nucleus of the system
The second is remarkable for its difference from the Kepleria
law, which states that

$$\overline{\Theta} \sim \mathscr{D}^{-\frac{1}{2}}.$$

The discrepancy shows the need for caution. It is not permissibl
without further thought, to identify the mean velocities wit
velocities of individual particles, determined by the law of motio
An earlier warning was given in § 2.6.

But we may, evidently, make use of the relations

$$\left. \begin{array}{l} \dfrac{\overline{\Theta}}{\mathscr{D}} = B - A, \\[4mm] \dfrac{d\overline{\Theta}}{d\mathscr{D}} = B + A, \end{array} \right\}$$

given in § 2.7. (The symbol u was used there, instead of $\overline{\Theta}$
The constants k_1 and k_2, appropriate to the Galaxy, can b
determined from these equations, and hence the value of th
function λ at the position of the Sun. Now $\sqrt{\lambda}$ is the ratio of th
Π-axis to the Θ-axis in the velocity ellipsoid, and the ratio i
also known from observation. We have a possibility here to tes
the applicability of the theory to the Galactic system.

From
$$\overline{\Theta} = \frac{k_1 \mathscr{D}}{1 + k_2 \mathscr{D}^2} = \frac{k_1 \mathscr{D}}{\lambda}$$

it follows that
$$\frac{d\overline{\Theta}}{d\mathscr{D}} = k_1 \frac{1 - k_2 \mathscr{D}^2}{(1 + k_2 \mathscr{D}^2)^2} = k_1 \frac{2 - \lambda}{\lambda^2},$$

and
$$\left. \begin{aligned} \left(\frac{k_1}{\lambda} \right)_\odot &= B - A, \\ \left(k_1 \frac{2 - \lambda}{\lambda^2} \right)_\odot &= B + A. \end{aligned} \right\}$$

On elimination of k_1 and solution for $\lambda_\odot$ we find that
$$\lambda_\odot = \frac{B - A}{B} \approx \frac{31}{13} = 2 \cdot 38 \dots$$

and
$$\sqrt{\lambda_\odot} = 1 \cdot 5 \dots.$$

The observed value is close to $28/20 = 1 \cdot 4$, so that there is adequate agreement between the model and observations. Incidentally $k_1 = \lambda_\odot^2 B$.

4. Two problems concerning our model remain to be clarified. (a) The Π- and Z-axes of the velocity ellipsoid are equal in the model, but not in reality, and (b) How do the high-velocity stars fit in?

The first point may be considered in the following way. For solutions with a constant $\mathscr{D}(t) = \mathscr{D}_0$ the third equation of motion reads
$$\ddot{Z} = -\frac{\partial}{\partial z} V(\mathscr{D}_0, z),$$

and has an "energy integral"
$$\begin{aligned} E_3 &= \tfrac{1}{2} \dot{z}^2 + V(\mathscr{D}_0, z) \\ &= \tfrac{1}{2} Z^2 + V(\mathscr{D}_0, z). \end{aligned}$$

For closely related motions, in which
$$| \mathscr{D}(t) - \mathscr{D}_0 | \ll \mathscr{D}_0$$

at all times, the function E_3, though no longer exactly constant, is yet approximately so, and is therefore an approximate integral.

I

Now add the term $k_3 E_3$ (with k_3 constant) to the integral Q the previous section. We thus obtain another approxima integral. With a suitable choice of k_3 the corresponding veloci surfaces become ellipsoids with three unequal axes and arbitrary ratio between the Π- and Z-axes. In the actual stell system the velocities have only a small scatter about their me value. Our approximate integral may therefore be used in t construction of a model.

The high-velocity stars can be represented in the frequen function by a second term of Schwarzschild's type having differe values for the constants. The discussion here is quite analog to that of the first term and need not be repeated. There a found to be very few stars whose tangential velocity componen in the direction of rotation exceed the average $|\overline{\Theta}|$ by mo than 60 km/s. The reason may be that this speed correspon to the "velocity of escape", or is a limiting speed beyond whi the gravitational forces of the whole system are no longer stro enough to retain the star concerned.

5. We now go on to consider the frequency function of stationary system with spherical symmetry. Let x_1, x_2, x_3 Cartesian coordinates, with their origin at the centre of t model, and r, ϕ, θ the corresponding polar coordinates. $R, \Phi,$ denote the appropriate linear velocity components. Let $V(r)$ the potential of a unit mass and $V'(r)$ its gradient.

The equations of motion

$$\left. \begin{aligned} \dot{u}_i &= -V'(r)\frac{x_i}{r}, \\ \dot{x}_i &= u_i, \qquad i = 1, 2, 3 \end{aligned} \right\}$$

have the energy integral

$$E = \tfrac{1}{2} u_j u_j + V(r)$$
$$= \tfrac{1}{2}(R^2 + \Phi^2 + \Theta^2) + V(r),$$

as well as the three area integrals

$$\left. \begin{aligned} F_1 &\equiv u_3 x_2 - u_2 x_3, \\ F_2 &\equiv u_1 x_3 - u_3 x_1, \\ F_3 &\equiv u_2 x_1 - u_1 x_2. \end{aligned} \right\}$$

The latter follow from the "rotational area integral" of § 3.2 simply by regarding each coordinate axis as an axis of symmetry.

The frequency function f is an integral of the equations of motion and, following III, § 2.2, it can be represented as a function of six independent integrals. But there cannot be six such integrals, all independent of the time. If these did exist, all solutions of the equations of motion would be time independent, and this is impossible. There are, therefore, at most five independent integrals which are not functions of the time. We only know four, and must content ourselves with them. We must then restrict ourselves to frequency functions of the form $f(E, F_1, F_2, F_3)$.

The spherical symmetry of the model requires that the frequency function f shall also possess spherical symmetry, and it will certainly do so if it has the form

$$f = f(E, F),$$

where F is the (positive) root of

$$F^2 = F_1^2 + F_2^2 + F_3^2.$$

For, in this case, $\qquad F^2 = r^2(\Phi^2 + \Theta^2),$

as is easily verified. If we introduce the transverse velocity

$$T = |\sqrt{(\Phi^2 + \Theta^2)}|,$$

then $\qquad F = rT,$

quite simply.

The converse theorem also holds. If the frequency function $f(E, F_1, F_2, F_3)$ does not depend on the angular coordinates ϕ and θ, it must be of the form $f(E, F)$.

To prove this, we use the conditions

$$\frac{\partial f}{\partial \phi} \equiv 0 \quad \text{and} \quad \frac{\partial f}{\partial \theta} \equiv 0,$$

and solve the resulting homogeneous system of linear equations

$$\frac{\partial f}{\partial F_j} \frac{\partial F_j}{\partial \phi} \equiv 0, \quad \frac{\partial f}{\partial F_j} \frac{\partial F_j}{\partial \theta} \equiv 0$$

for the derivatives $\partial f/\partial F_i$. The coefficients $\partial F_i/\partial \phi$ and $\partial F_i/\partial \theta$ a
calculated from the representations

$$\left.\begin{aligned}
F_1 &\equiv r(-\Phi \sin\theta\cos\phi + \Theta \sin\phi), \\
F_2 &\equiv r(\Phi \sin\theta\sin\phi + \Theta \cos\phi), \\
F_3 &\equiv r\Phi \cos\theta.
\end{aligned}\right\}$$

The coefficients are found to be

$$\left.\begin{aligned}
\frac{\partial F_1}{\partial\phi} &= F_2, & \frac{\partial F_1}{\partial\theta} &= -F_3\cos\phi, \\
\frac{\partial F_2}{\partial\phi} &= -F_1, & \frac{\partial F_2}{\partial\theta} &= F_3\sin\phi, \\
\frac{\partial F_3}{\partial\phi} &= 0, & \frac{\partial F_3}{\partial\theta} &= F_1\cos\phi - F_2\sin\phi,
\end{aligned}\right\}$$

and the solution of the equations is

$$\frac{\partial f}{\partial F_1} : \frac{\partial f}{\partial F_2} : \frac{\partial f}{\partial F_3} = F_1 : F_2 : F_3.$$

This implies that, in a three-dimensional euclidian space wi
orthogonal coordinates (F_1, F_2, F_3), the surfaces $f(E, F_1, F_2, F_3)$ a
everywhere perpendicular to the position vectors (F_1, F_2, F_3), an
are therefore spherical. The function f is constant on every sphe

$$F^2 \equiv F_1^2 + F_2^2 + F_3^2 = \text{const},$$

and is a function of F only, as stated.

In future we shall refer to F simply as the area integral.

6. We may consider frequency functions of the form $f = f(Q)$
where
$$Q = 2E - 2k_1F + k_2F^2,$$

for models with spherical symmetry, in the same way as we d
in the case of rotational symmetry (§ 3.3). However, we obta
ellipsoidal velocity surfaces only when $k_1 = 0$. The explic
formula for the integral Q is

$$Q = R^2 + \lambda(T - T_0)^2 + 2V(r) - \frac{k_1^2 r^2}{\lambda}$$

$$= R^2 + \lambda\{|\sqrt{(\Phi^2 + \Theta^2)}| - T_0\}^2 + 2V(r) - \frac{k_1^2 r^2}{\lambda},$$

where we have put $$\lambda = 1 + k_2 r^2$$

and $$T_0 = \frac{k_1 r}{\lambda}.$$

Once again we require $\lambda > 0$.

The velocity surfaces in (R, Φ, Θ) space are obtained, from the curves $Q = $ const in the (R, T) plane, by rotation about the R-axis. When $k_1 = 0$, these curves are ellipses with major and minor axes along the coordinate axes. Otherwise, when $k_1 > 0$, the curve $Q = $ const would also be an ellipse, with the T-axis as major axis, if T could assume all possible values. But only non-negative values of T can occur on the velocity surfaces, since T was defined to be the magnitude of a speed. If, therefore, T were to extend into the lower half plane, $T < 0$, the arc of the ellipse lying there would have to be cut off. Since T_0 is positive, the centre $(0, T_0)$ of the ellipse is above the R-axis. The rotation of the upper arc of the ellipse about the R-axis would therefore generate a velocity surface with singular points on that axis.

In almost every case where $k_1 > 0$, it may be shown that there are point sets for which $Q = $ const, which can only be described by elliptical arcs, but not by whole ellipses. When $k_1 \neq 0$ there are thus always velocity surfaces with singularities, which one will usually wish to avoid. Care must therefore be exercised in framing a hypothesis concerning the frequency function. We may note that our intuitive deduction of § 3.1, showing the velocity surfaces to be ellipsoidal in a first approximation, was only valid in the absence of singularities.

7. One would expect a velocity distribution of Schwarzschild's type in the case of systems with spherical symmetry, just as in the case of the Galactic System. One would assume the existence of ellipsoidal velocity surfaces, that is, of surfaces defined by constant values of the integral

$$Q = 2E + k_2 F^2.$$

One would then write

$$f(Q) = \text{const.} \exp[-Q/\sigma^2], \qquad \sigma = \text{const.} > 0,$$

or, rather, build up frequency functions by adding together several terms of this kind, each possibly referring to stars of a particular spectral type. A full discussion of this hypothesis involves the use of Poisson's equation and is postponed to § 4.

4. Poisson's equation

1. We begin with a further study of stationary systems possessing spherical symmetry. For them the gravitational potential $V(r)$ satisfies Poisson's equation

$$\frac{d^2 V}{dr^2} + \frac{2}{r}\frac{dV}{dr} = 4\pi G\rho,$$

according to IV, § 1.3, where the density is

$$\rho = \iiint_{-\infty}^{\infty} f\, dR\, d\Phi\, d\Theta.$$

The frequency function f is assumed to be given as a function $f(E, F)$ of the energy and area integrals. Evidently ρ is then a function of V and r. We introduce it into Poisson's equation and find

$$\frac{d^2 V}{dr^2} + \frac{2}{r}\frac{dV}{dr} = 4\pi G\rho(V, r),$$

or

$$\left.\begin{aligned}\frac{dV'}{dr} &= 4\pi G\rho(V, r) - \frac{2V'}{r},\\[2mm]\frac{dV}{dr} &= V'.\end{aligned}\right\}$$

Owing to its singularity near $r = 0$ this second-order system of differential equations does not satisfy the conditions of III, § 2.1. However, the existence of a unique solution can be established even so, provided one of the initial conditions is that $V'(0) = 0$. The formal significance of this condition is that the singularity has been "removed"; its mechanical significance is that the gravitational field strength vanishes at the centre. This is certainly the case, and follows from IV, § 1.3, or quite readily from symmetry considerations. The second initial condition is $V(0) = 0$. This is arbitrary, since any desired constant can be added to the potential without affecting the mechanical state of the system.

The calculation of a model is carried out as follows. A reasonable looking frequency function $f(E, F)$ is assumed and the density function $\rho(V, r)$ evaluated. The resulting Poisson's equation is solved and, by introducing its solution into the energy integral, we can then obtain an explicit expression for the frequency function. All the other properties of the model may now be found as well.

But a problem arises here. It can (and does in fact) happen that an unreasonable model is derived from a reasonable looking frequency function $f(E, F)$. This only becomes apparent after the calculations have been finished (if that is possible). Is there any way of seeing whether a function f is useful before going through a calculation?

In order to sharpen the concept of "reasonableness" we shall consider an example.

2. The exponential hypothesis

$$f = \text{const.} \exp[-E/\sigma^2], \qquad \sigma = \text{const} > 0,$$

was previously mentioned in § 3.7, and has been used a number of times. The corresponding density function is

$$\rho = \text{const.} \exp[-V/\sigma^2],$$

and Poisson's equation becomes

$$\frac{d^2 V}{dr^2} + \frac{2}{r} \frac{dV}{dr} = \text{const.} \exp[-V/\sigma^2],$$

$$V(0) = 0, \quad V'(0) = 0.$$

This equation is well known from other studies. It is satisfied by the gravitational potential of a mass of gas with spherical symmetry, which has a uniform temperature and in which gravitation and gas pressure balance one another.

Now it may be shown that the appropriate density function $\rho\{V(r)\}$ is asymptotically proportional to $1/r^2$ as $r \to \infty$. Hence the mass

$$m(r) = 4\pi \int_0^r \rho\{V(s)\} s^2 ds,$$

which is contained within a sphere of radius r, tends to infinity as $r \to \infty$. A model of infinite total mass is not useful in practice. The assumed frequency function cannot be held to be reasonable.

Our requirement is therefore that the function $f(E, F)$ shall be so chosen that the model has a finite total mass.

Apart from this the density variation of this "isothermal gas sphere" does not tally with that measured in real globular clusters, as far as it has been observed. Admittedly only the very brightest, and therefore only the most massive stars can be seen in these systems, but even they should follow the isothermal density law if it were at all suitable. Thus observation also shows the uselessness of the exponential hypothesis.

3. We may derive a necessary condition for a finite total mass in this way.

We first of all show that the potential $V(r)$ has a finite limit

$$V_\infty = \lim_{r \to \infty} V(r)$$

when the total mass m_∞ is finite. For, writing Poisson's equation in the form

$$\frac{1}{r^2} \frac{\mathrm{d}}{\mathrm{d}r}\left(r^2 \frac{\mathrm{d}V}{\mathrm{d}r}\right) = 4\pi G \rho, \qquad \rho = \rho(r),$$

we have, on integration, that

$$r^2 \frac{\mathrm{d}V}{\mathrm{d}r} = 4\pi G \int_0^r \rho(s)\, s^2 \,\mathrm{d}s$$

$$= G m(r).$$

For $r \geqslant r_1 > 0$ we then find that

$$0 < \frac{\mathrm{d}V}{\mathrm{d}r} = G\frac{m(r)}{r^2} \leqslant G\frac{m_\infty}{r^2},$$

$$V(r) = V(r_1) + \int_{r_1}^r G\frac{m(s)}{s^2}\,\mathrm{d}s$$

$$\leqslant V(r_1) + G m_\infty \int_{r_1}^r \frac{\mathrm{d}s}{s^2}$$

$$= V(r_1) + G m_\infty \left(\frac{1}{r_1} - \frac{1}{r}\right).$$

$V(r)$ is thus a monotonically increasing function with an upper bound. The assertion is therefore proved.

We now assert that, if $f(E, F)$ is the frequency function of a model with a finite total mass m_∞, then $f(E, F) = 0$ for all pairs (E, F) in which $E \geqslant V_\infty$.

Suppose that this assertion is false. Then there is at least one pair of values (E_0, F_0), with $E_0 \geqslant V_\infty$, for which f is positive, say

$$f(E_0, F_0) \geqslant 2\alpha,$$

where α is a positive constant. Owing to the continuity of f it may be assumed, without loss of generality, that $E_0 > V_\infty$ and $F_0 > 0$. In addition there will be a certain region surrounding (E_0, F_0) in which f is positive, so that

$$f(E, F) > \alpha,$$

when $\qquad\qquad |E - E_0| < \delta, \quad |F^2 - F_0^2| < k\delta,$

where δ is a positive number which may depend on E_0, F_0 and α. The positive constant k is included for dimensional reasons. We note, for later use, that the inequality $f > \alpha$ remains valid if δ is replaced by any smaller quantity with the same dimensions.

The inequality

$$f(\tfrac{1}{2}R^2 + \tfrac{1}{2}T^2 + V(r), rT) > \alpha$$

is satisfied when

$$\left.\begin{array}{l} 2E_0 - 2V(r) - 2\delta < R^2 + T^2 < 2E_0 - 2V(r) + 2\delta, \\[2mm] 0 < F_0^2 - k\delta < r^2 T^2 < F_0^2 + k\delta, \end{array}\right\}$$

and

where $k\delta$ is chosen smaller than F_0^2.

But $V(r)$ increases monotonically with r. We now determine a number $r_0 = r_0(\delta)$, such that

$$0 < V_\infty - V < \delta$$

for all $r > r_0$, and use it to limit more closely the region within which the inequality $f > \alpha$ is valid. Evidently

$$f(\tfrac{1}{2}R^2 + \tfrac{1}{2}T^2 + V(r), rT) > \alpha$$

when

$$\left.\begin{array}{c} 2E_0 - 2V_\infty < R^2 + T^2 < 2E_0 - 2V_\infty + 2\delta \\[2mm] 0 < \dfrac{F_0^2 - k\delta}{r^2} < T^2 < \dfrac{F_0^2 + k\delta}{r^2} \\[2mm] r \geqslant r_0. \end{array}\right\}$$

and

The second inequality is now used to limit still further the range of variation of R^2. We have that $f > \alpha$ for

$$R_1^2 < R^2 < R_2^2, \quad T_1^2 < T^2 < T_2^2, \quad r \geqslant r_0,$$

where

$$\left. \begin{array}{ll} R_1^2 = 2E_0 - 2V_\infty - \dfrac{F_0^2 - k\delta}{r^2}, & R_2^2 = 2E_0 - 2V_\infty - \dfrac{F_0^2 + k\delta}{r^2} + 2\delta, \\[2mm] T_1^2 = \dfrac{F_0^2 - k\delta}{r^2}, & T_2^2 = \dfrac{F_0^2 + k\delta}{r^2}. \end{array} \right\}$$

In order to make $\quad R_2^2 - R_1^2 = 2\delta(1 - k/r^2)$

positive, we must choose $r_0^2 > k$.

The mass density $\rho = \rho(r)$ can be represented by

$$\rho(r) = \iiint_{-\infty}^{\infty} f\{\tfrac{1}{2}R^2 + \tfrac{1}{2}\Phi^2 + \tfrac{1}{2}\Theta^2 + V(r),\ r\,|\sqrt{(\Phi^2 + \Theta^2)}|\}\,\mathrm{d}R\,\mathrm{d}\Phi\,\mathrm{d}\Theta$$

$$= 2\pi \iint f\{\tfrac{1}{2}R^2 + \tfrac{1}{2}T^2 + V(r),\ rT\}\,\mathrm{d}R \quad T\,\mathrm{d}T$$

$$\geqslant 2\pi \int_{R_1}^{R_2}\mathrm{d}R \int_{T_1}^{T_2} f \quad T\,\mathrm{d}T$$

$$> 2\pi\alpha \int_{R_1}^{R_2}\mathrm{d}R \int_{T_1}^{T_2} T\,\mathrm{d}T$$

$$= \pi\alpha(R_2 - R_1)(T_2^2 - T_1^2)$$

$$= \pi\alpha(R_2 - R_1)\cdot\frac{2k\delta}{r^2}.$$

But $R_2^2 - R_1^2$ possesses a positive lower bound, whose value is $2\delta(1 - k/r_0^2)$, for all $r \geqslant r_0$, and so does $R_2 - R_1$. Let the bound equal β, then

$$\rho(r) > \pi\alpha\beta\cdot\frac{2k\delta}{r^2},$$

and it follows that

$$m(r) = 4\pi \int_0^r \rho(s)\,s^2\,\mathrm{d}s$$

$$= m(r_0) + 4\pi \int_{r_0}^r \rho(s)\,s^2\,\mathrm{d}s$$

$$\geqslant m(r_0) + 4\pi^2\alpha\beta\cdot 2k\delta(r - r_0),$$

for $r \geqslant r_0$. Hence $m(r) \to \infty$ as $r \to \infty$.

The result means that our initial hypothesis contradicts the assumption of a finite total mass. This proves our assertion that there must be an upper bound to the energy of the various elements of mass in the system.

It is conceivable that $f(E, F)$ might vanish identically, not only for all $E \geqslant V_\infty$, but possibly for all $E \geqslant B$, where $0 < B < V_\infty$. The lower bound A of all the possible numbers B of this type will be called the zero position of the frequency function $f(E, F)$. We must, of course, assume that $A > 0$, or else we should find that $f \equiv 0$.

The model evidently has a finite radius r_* when $A < V_\infty$, and an infinite radius when $A = V_\infty$.

4. The last theorem shows why the exponential law

$$f = \mathrm{const} \times \exp[-E/\sigma^2]$$

leads to an infinite total mass: the frequency function has no zero in this case. This would still be true if the function were a sum of several exponential expressions with positive coefficients— as would happen, for example, if every term of the sum were to represent a certain class of star. If, however, negative coefficients did occur and the polynomial could take negative values, then we should have to replace it by, say, $f \equiv 0$, from the first zero onwards.

Every frequency function f vanishes for sufficiently large E, and so none can be an analytic function. It can, at most, be piecewise analytic, the last piece always being zero.

It may further be shown that there is no model with a finite total mass which corresponds to a frequency function of the type $f(E - kF^2)$, where k is positive. For suppose that there were values E_1 and F_1, with

$$A \geqslant E_1 \geqslant 0, \quad F_1 \geqslant 0,$$

for which

$$f(E_1 - kF_1^2) > 0,$$

then we should have

$$f(A - kF_2^2) > 0,$$

where

$$F_2^2 = F_1^2 + \frac{A - E_1}{k} \geqslant 0,$$

because

$$A - kF_2^2 = E_1 - kF_1^2.$$

The inequality $f(A - kF_{\frac{3}{2}}^2) > 0$ contradicts the theorem proved in Section 3.

On the other hand the following statement can be proved: If a frequency function $f(E)$ corresponds to a model with a finite radius, then so does a frequency function $f(E + kF^2)$, where k is a small enough positive quantity. We omit the proof.

5. As the most important example of a frequency function, in particular one of the type $f(E)$, we shall now consider the function

$$f = \begin{cases} (A - E)^n, & \text{for } E \leqslant A, \\ 0, & \text{for } E > A, \end{cases}$$

where n is a positive constant. The necessary condition for a finite total mass is evidently fulfilled. We find that the mass density equals

$$\rho = 2\pi \iint (A - V - \tfrac{1}{2}R^2 - \tfrac{1}{2}T^2)^n \, T \, dR \, dT,$$

the integral being taken over the upper semicircle of

$$\tfrac{1}{2}(R^2 + T^2) \leqslant A - V.$$

On introducing polar coordinates (v, θ) in the (R, T)-plane we find

$$\rho = 2\pi \int_0^{\sqrt{2(A-V)}} \int_0^\pi (A - V - \tfrac{1}{2}v^2)^n \, v^2 \sin\theta \, dv \, d\theta$$

$$= 4\pi \int_0^{\sqrt{2(A-V)}} (A - V - \tfrac{1}{2}v^2)^n \, v^2 \, dv$$

$$= 4\pi \cdot 2^{\frac{3}{2}} \int_0^1 (A - V)^{n+\frac{3}{2}} (1 - s^2)^n s^2 \, ds,$$

where

$$s = \frac{v}{\sqrt{\{2(A - V)\}}}.$$

Hence

$$\rho = (A - V)^{n+\frac{3}{2}} \cdot 2^{\frac{3}{2}} \cdot 4\pi \int_0^1 (1 - s^2)^n s^2 \, ds,$$

or finally

$$\rho = c_n u^{n+\frac{3}{2}},$$

where

$$u = 1 - \frac{V}{A}$$

and

$$c_n = A^{n+\frac{3}{2}} \cdot 2^{\frac{3}{2}} \cdot 4\pi \int_0^1 (1 - s^2)^n s^2 \, ds.$$

We introduce these expressions for V and ρ into Poisson's equation

$$\frac{d^2 V}{dr^2} + \frac{2}{r}\frac{dV}{dr} = 4\pi G\rho,$$

and find that

$$\frac{d^2 u}{ds^2} + \frac{2}{n}\frac{du}{ds} + u^{n+\frac{3}{2}} = 0,$$

the dimensionless variable s in this last equation being defined by

$$s = r\left(\frac{A}{2\pi Gc_n}\right).$$

The corresponding initial conditions are

$$u = 1, \quad \frac{du}{ds} = 0 \quad \text{when} \quad s = 0.$$

The differential equation in u is that of a polytropic gas sphere of index $(n+\frac{3}{2})$. By the expression "polytropic gas sphere of index i" we mean a mass of gas with spherical symmetry, in which the gas pressure balances the gravitational forces, and in which the local pressure is proportional to $\rho^{1+(1/i)}$, ρ being the local density. The equation refers to the gravitational potential. It is assumed that i is positive.

Fowler and E. Hopf have established that the sphere corresponding to this equation has a finite radius when the index $i = n+\frac{3}{2} \leqslant 3$. Emden argued from a graphical representation that this is probably true even when $3 < n+\frac{3}{2} < 5$. In the case $n+\frac{3}{2} = 5$ the model can be represented explicitly by means of elementary functions, and it then has an infinite radius, but a finite mass. It seems plausible that the models, for which $n+\frac{3}{2} > 5$, have infinite radii and masses.

These results establish, in the first place, the existence of a class of reasonable models, namely the polytropic models with index $n+\frac{3}{2} \leqslant 3$ (or even < 5). These models have a finite radius r_*. They do not have a sharp boundary; that is to say, the density gradient vanishes at the boundary. It seems that they represent quite well those density variations which have been observed in real globular clusters.

6. The models can thus be used, for example, in estimates of masses. As in IV, § 4.3, the formulae obtained are again of the form

$$m_\infty = \text{const.} \frac{r_* \overline{R^2}}{G}.$$

The dimensionless factor of proportionality is of the order unity; its exact value depends on the particular model. It may be estimated as follows: A polytropic gas sphere of index $i = m + \frac{3}{2} < 5$ has the potential energy

$$U = -\frac{3}{5-i} \frac{Gm_\infty^2}{r_*}.$$

(A proof of this relation may be found in the literature.) According to the virial theorem of IV, § 4.2 (here used for once with a continuum model) we have

$$2T + E = 0$$

so that

$$3m_\infty \overline{R^2} - \frac{3}{5-i} \frac{Gm_\infty^2}{r_*} = 0$$

and finally

$$m_\infty = (5-i) \frac{r_* \overline{R^2}}{G}.$$

In any application it must be remembered that radial velocities cannot be measured in the nucleus of the cluster, where they are largest. The observationally found value of $\overline{R^2}$ is therefore almost certainly too small. In a more exact calculation one must consequently make use of the frequency function to find the mean radial velocity in that part of the system which is actually being observed.

7. We have, earlier, found a condition which must be fulfilled if the total mass is to be finite. The condition does not, however, appear to be sufficient. For example, the frequency function $(A - E)^4$ corresponds to a polytropic gas sphere of index 5·5, whose mass is, presumably, infinite.

It can, nevertheless, be shown that the necessary condition is also sufficient in practice and in this sense. Given any frequency function $f(E, F)$ which satisfies the necessary condition we can define a second frequency function $\tilde{f}(E, F)$ which differs arbitrarily little from $f(E, F)$, for all non-negative E and F, and which corresponds to a model of finite mass and, even, finite radius. We can therefore state, roughly, that all models with a finite radius form a dense subset in the set of all the models which satisfy the necessary condition. This formulation can easily be made more precise.

The basis of the proof is as follows. Let

$$f(E, F) = \begin{cases} (A - E)^n g(E, F) & \text{for} \quad E \leqslant A, \\ 0 & \text{for} \quad E > A, \end{cases}$$

be the given frequency function. The constant n is taken to be larger than unity, at first. Let δ be an arbitrarily small positive constant, and $\tilde{A}$ an arbitrary constant larger than A, but possibly differing from it by only a very small amount. Let m be a constant between 1 and $\min(n, \frac{3}{2})$. We then put

$$\tilde{f}(E, F) = \begin{cases} f(E, F) + \delta(\tilde{A} - E)^m, & E \leqslant \tilde{A}, \\ 0 & , \quad E > \tilde{A}. \end{cases}$$

Evidently $\tilde{f}$ satisfies the necessary condition and differs by only a little from the given function f. Now it can be shown that the potential $\tilde{V}$ belonging to $\tilde{f}$ will exceed A for sufficiently large radial distances r. For such values of r the model belonging to the frequency function $\tilde{f}$ is thus determined by a Poisson's equation identical with that for a polytropic gas sphere of index $m + \frac{3}{2} \leqslant 3$. This is not true, in general, for small r. The critical value r_1 is defined uniquely by the equation $\tilde{V}(r_1) = A$. For $r \geqslant r_1$ the model corresponds to a polytropic gas sphere with a solid core. Such a model gas sphere is useful, for instance, in describing an atmosphere with a polytropic structure, surrounding a solid planet. E. Hopf has shown that it has a finite radius if the index is not larger than 3. The same is true of our model, which belongs to the frequency function f. This completes the proof.

The case $n = 1$, which we excluded above, can now be treated similarly, use being made of our result for $n > 1$.

We have now established the following general result concerning all the models of finite radius. The frequency function must satisfy the necessary condition if the mass and, *a fortiori*, the radius are to be finite. The energies of all the elements of mass must therefore be uniformly bounded. Conversely, given any frequency function for which the uniform bound exists, an arbitrarily small alteration will change it into the frequency function of a model of finite radius.

The envelopes of all the models have a polytropic, or a similar, structure. The reason for this is that, when $r(\leqslant r_* < \infty)$ is large enough, the frequency function

$$f = (A - E)^n g(E, F), \qquad E \leqslant A$$

does not differ materially from the frequency function

$$f^* = (A - E)^n g(A, F), \qquad E \leqslant A.$$

In the calculation of the corresponding density function, the values of F in question are all near zero, for it follows from $r = r_*$ that $E = A$, $T^2 = 0$ and so $F = 0$. The model therefore has a density function close to that of a model with the frequency function

$$f^* = (A - E)^n g(A, 0), \qquad E \leqslant A.$$

For large values of r Poisson's equation thus corresponds closely to the equation for a polytropic gas sphere (with or without a solid core). Observation seems to bear this out, as was stated before.

8. We shall now study the motion of an individual element of mass in a model with a finite radius r_*.

It is physically evident, and easily shown formally, that the motion of an element must be in the plane which contains the centre of the model and the initial position of the element, and which is parallel to its initial velocity. Three types of motion are thus possible:

(a) rest at the central point;

(b) motion along a straight line through the central point;

(c) motion in a plane through the central point along a trajectory not passing through that point.

Now take cartesian axes, with the trajectory lying in the $(1, 2)$-plane, and introduce the corresponding polar coordinates

(r, ϕ, θ). The polar coordinates of our mass element then satisfy the energy and the area theorems, in the form

$$\left.\begin{array}{l} \tfrac{1}{2}\dot{r}^2 + \tfrac{1}{2}r^2\dot{\phi}^2 + V(r) = E_0, \\ r^2\dot{\phi} \qquad\qquad = F_0, \end{array}\right\}$$

where E_0 and F_0 are two non-negative constants. The case (a) corresponds to $E_0 = 0$. Case (a) or case (b) corresponds to $F_0 = 0$. We shall first consider case (c), in which $E_0, F_0 \neq 0$.

It is physically clear that the trajectory is always concave towards the central point. The formal proof of this is omitted here.

We shall now demonstrate that every trajectory oscillates between two fixed circles $r = r_1$ and $r = r_2$. To this end we eliminate the angular velocity $\dot{\phi}$ from the energy and the area equations and find

$$\tfrac{1}{2}\dot{r}^2 = E_0 - V(r) - \frac{1}{2}\frac{F_0^2}{r^2} \equiv \tfrac{1}{2}\psi(r).$$

We now prove the lemma that the function $\psi(r)$ has exactly two zeros for $r > 0$, and that these either coincide or are of the first order. We shall treat only the second possibility; the other may be considered as one of its limiting cases. The function $\psi(r)$ is negative for very small and for very large positive r. It cannot, however, be negative for all r, in particular for those r which correspond to the possible positions of our element of mass—otherwise we should find imaginary radial velocities. Hence $\psi(r)$ has at least two zeros at r_1 and r_2, where $0 < r_1 \leqslant r_2 < r_*$. We shall show that there are exactly two zeros, both of the first order.

We differentiate $\psi(r)$ with respect to r and find

$$\frac{1}{2}\frac{\mathrm{d}}{\mathrm{d}r}\psi(r) = -\frac{\mathrm{d}}{\mathrm{d}r}V(r) + \frac{F_0^2}{r^3}.$$

Now Poisson's equation states that

$$\frac{\mathrm{d}}{\mathrm{d}r}V(r) = G\frac{m(r)}{r^2}.$$

Hence

$$\tfrac{1}{2}r^3\frac{\mathrm{d}\psi}{\mathrm{d}r} = F_0^2 - Grm(r).$$

K

The right-hand side is a continuous and strictly monotonically decreasing function of r. Now $d\psi/dr$, and therefore also $r^3(d\psi/dr)$, has at least one zero between r_1 and r_2, the two zeros of $\psi(r)$ (Rolle's theorem). This is also the only zero, owing to the strictly monotonic decrease. It follows that r_1 and r_2 are the only zeros of $\psi(r)$, and that they are simple.

Let the element of mass have a radial distance r_0, between r_1 and r_2, at time t_0. (If r_1 and r_2 coincide, the element moves along a circle and nothing remains to be proved.) If $\dot{r}(t_0) > 0$, say, the element will reach the circle $r = r_2$ within a finite interval of time, as we shall now show. It follows from

$$\dot{r}^2 = \psi(r)$$

that
$$t - t_0 = \int_{r_0}^{r} \frac{dr}{\sqrt{\{\psi(r)\}}} \,;$$

in particular, when t equals t_2, the time of arrival,

$$t_2 - t_0 = \int_{r_0}^{r_2} \frac{dr}{\sqrt{\{\psi(r)\}}}.$$

According to the result we have proved, $\psi(r)$ can be represented in the interval $r_0 \ldots r_2$, by

$$\psi(r) = (r - r_2)\,\psi'(r_2) + O(r - r_2)$$
$$= (r_2 - r)\,|\,\psi'(r_2)\,|\,.\,[1 + O(1)],$$

ψ' being the derivative of ψ with respect to r. (We recall here that $\psi'(r_2)$ is negative.) On introduction of this expression for $\psi(r)$ into the equation for $t_2 - t_0$ we find that

$$t_2 - t_0 = \frac{2\sqrt{(r_2 - r_0)}}{\sqrt{\{|\,\psi'(r_2)|\}}} \times \{1 + O(1)\},$$

and this is finite.

When $t > t_2$, $r(t)$ falls to the value r_1 in a finite time. This may be proved in a quite similar way. After reaching r_1, $r(t)$ begins to increase again. It is seen that $r(t)$ is a periodic function of the time, with the half-period

$$\int_{r_1}^{r_2} \frac{dr}{\sqrt{\{\psi(r)\}}}.$$

The half-period is the time required by the element to move from one circle to the other.

The angular velocity

$$\dot{\phi}(t) = \frac{F_0}{\{r(t)\}^2}$$

s also a periodic function of the time, with the same half-period.
If we expand the function in a Fourier series, and integrate, we
find that the angle $\phi(t)$ is the sum of a linear function and of a
periodic function of the time.

We deduce that all curved trajectories must have an oval or a
rosette-like shape. The rectilinear trajectories (b) can be considered as limiting cases, and they, also, are described in periodic
motions.

Two cases are to be distinguished in the case of rosette orbits,
depending on whether the angle δ, by which $\phi(t)$ increases in
one period, is or is not commensurable with a right angle. In the
first case the trajectories are closed. In the second case it can be
shown that the trajectory comes arbitrarily close to every point
in the ring $r_1 \leqslant r \leqslant r_2$ and, further, that almost all the trajectories
are in fact open rosettes like this. These idealized mathematical
results are not significant in astronomical applications, and we
shall not give their proofs here.

We close this section with an estimate of the angle δ, whose
value largely determines the shape of a trajectory. If the mass
of the system were concentrated entirely at its central point, then
all the trajectories would be Kepler ellipses, and δ would equal 2π.
If the material were uniformly spread out, the gravitational field
intensity would everywhere be proportional to the position vector.
The resulting trajectories would be ellipses with their centres at
the central point of the system. In this case δ would equal π.
It seems, therefore, plausible that the angle δ lies between π
and 2π when the density function $\rho(r)$ decreases strictly monotonically. A proof of this result can be constructed, but is
omitted here.

9. We shall now consider stationary models with one axis of
rotational symmetry. In § 3 we treated such models purely from
the point of view of the fundamental theorem, and arrived at
some detailed conclusions. But conditions are completely different
when we take into account the self-gravitation of the various

systems, by means of Poisson's equation. All the earlier results are now uncertain, in the sense that they are valid only if the corresponding models "exist" or, in other words, if they have reasonable properties. It is not known at present whether they do, in fact, do so.

In the case of systems with spherical symmetry, one property of a reasonable model was that it had a finite mass or a finite radius. In the case of systems with rotational symmetry it is appropriate to introduce, from the beginning, the stronger condition that the system shall have only a finite extent. The reason for this is that only masses in certain limited regions are effective in the dynamics of systems with spherical symmetry. (The regions are spheres with their centres at the central point.) Whether the system extends to infinity or not, and whether it has a finite or an infinite mass, is only of minor importance for the nature of its inner motions. In a structure with a more general shape this limitation to only a part of the system is no longer feasible. The local forces are determined by the distribution of mass in the whole system in such a way that a change anywhere in it affects the forces at every other point. If the model were to extend to infinity, it would be difficult to say whether the forces are, for example, finite and uniquely determined at all its points. We therefore find it better to assume, from the beginning, that the mass density $\rho(x)$ of the model is positive only in a finite region of the position space Γ_x.

This leads to a new difficulty, for only the form $f(E, F_3)$ of the distribution function is known, and not even the function f is given. How can the function be chosen to yield a model which is limited in our sense?

Even if this were done we still could not determine the boundary of the model; the only fact known about would be that it must be a surface of constant potential. Failing this, a flow would result with a tendency to even out the differences of potential; the system would then be non-stationary.

Our remarks show the extraordinary mathematical difficulties opposing the construction of these models. In fact the problems of existence and uniqueness have not yet been solved for any model or any given frequency function $f(E, F_3)$. The next section contains a summary of what little is known.

We may remark that the assumed form $f(E, F_3)$ of the distribution function is of a special kind, f being a function of only two time-independent integrals of the equations of motion. We have to be content with these, as we were in our treatment of spherically symmetrical models, for we know of no other integrals which are suitable (i.e. are single-valued in all phase-space).

10. Let us assume that we are given a "limited" stationary model with rotational symmetry, and with the frequency function $f(E, F_3)$. Let the potential $V(x)$ be so defined that zero is its smallest value, attained at the central point of the system. Let this point also be chosen as the origin of coordinates. Then

$$V(x) = G \int_{\Gamma_\xi} \rho(\xi) \left\{ \frac{1}{|\xi|} - \frac{1}{|x - \xi|} \right\} d\xi.$$

(Cf. § 5.2 for the formulation.) It is assumed that the frequency function $f(E, F_3)$ is defined for all $E \geqslant 0$ and all F_3. We then state first of all:

The function $f(E, F_3)$ equals zero for all E exceeding a certain constant A, and the function is positive for values of E which are less than A by a small amount. If S is the region in which the mass density is positive, then

$$A = \sup_{x \in S} V(x) < V_\infty = G \int_{\Gamma_\xi} \frac{\rho(\xi)}{|\xi|} d\xi < \infty.$$

The proof is indirect. Suppose that we have $f(E_0, F_0) > 0$ for a pair of values (E_0, F_0), where $E_0 \geqslant V_\infty$. To this pair there corresponds a point $(\overset{\circ}{u}, \overset{\circ}{x})$ in phase space, which can evidently be chosen in such a way that $\overset{\circ}{x}$ lies outside S. The function f is then positive in a sufficiently small neighbourhood of $(\overset{\circ}{u}, \overset{\circ}{x})$ in Γ. The density $\rho_0(x)$ is also positive in a sufficiently small neighbourhood of $\overset{\circ}{x}$ in Γ_x. This contradicts the assumption that $\overset{\circ}{x}$ is outside S. It follows that f vanishes for sufficiently large values of E. The remainder of the statement is now obvious.

This theorem is analogous to that of Section 3, concerning systems with spherical symmetry. The conditions were, however, less restrictive in the latter, since it was only required that the mass should be finite. If finite dimensions are also postulated here, then the present proof can be taken over without change.

We now state, in analogy to Section 4, that there is no limited model with a frequency function of type $f(Q)$, where

$$Q = 2E - 2k_1 F_3 - k_2 F_3^2$$

$$= \Pi^2 + Z^2 + (1 - k_2 \mathscr{D}^2) \left(\Theta - \frac{k_1 \mathscr{D}}{1 - k_2 \mathscr{D}^2} \right)^2 - \frac{k_1^2 \mathscr{D}^2}{1 - k_2 \mathscr{D}^2} + 2V(\mathscr{D}, z),$$

and $$k_1 \geqslant 0, \quad k_2 > 0.$$

The proof is indirect. If there were a frequency function like this, then it would follow from the previous theorem that

$$f(2A - 2k_1 F_3 - k_2 F_3^2) = 0, \quad \text{for all} \quad F_3.$$

Now suppose there to be a pair of values (E_0, F_0), with $0 \leqslant E_0 < A$, such that $$f(2E_0 - 2k_1 F_0 - k_2 F_0^2) > 0.$$

We now seek a value F_1 for which

$$2A - 2k_1 F_1 - k_2 F_1^2 = 2E_0 - 2k_1 F_0 - k_2 F_0^2.$$

If this were possible we should have found a contradiction, for $f(Q)$ would be positive and zero for the same value of the argument. But the required value of F_1 can, indeed, be found, as is easily verified.

There are further problems: Do any such models exist? What are the sufficient conditions for their existence? How many models can correspond to a given frequency function $f(E, F_3)$? All these questions are as yet unanswered, as we pointed out earlier. In particular, we still are not certain of the correctness, or otherwise, of Jeans' assertion that a frequency function of the form $f(E)$ necessarily leads to a spherically symmetrical model. If this were so, spherical symmetry in velocity space Γ_u would imply spherical symmetry in position space Γ_x.

11. In the same way there is very little known about the trajectories of the elements of mass in stationary models with rotational symmetry. It is, however, clear that trajectories in the equatorial plane can be treated in the same way as the orbits in systems with spherical symmetry (Section 7). The general case will again be the rosette-like orbit; the other possibilities are all special cases. No investigations seem to have yet been made into the general character of the orbits outside the equatorial plane.

An approximate calculation can readily be made to determine orbits which are close to circles in the equatorial plane. The equations of motion

$$\ddot{x}_i = -\frac{\partial V}{\partial x_i}, \qquad i = 1, 2, 3,$$

are transformed to cylindrical coordinates and then linearized. The transformed equations are

$$
\left.
\begin{aligned}
\ddot{\mathcal{D}} - \mathcal{D}\dot{\theta}^2 &= -\frac{\partial V}{\partial \mathcal{D}}, \\
2\dot{\mathcal{D}}\dot{\theta} + \mathcal{D}\ddot{\theta} &= 0, \\
\ddot{z} &= -\frac{\partial V}{\partial z}.
\end{aligned}
\right\}
$$

The circular motions in question are determined by

$$
\left.
\begin{aligned}
\mathcal{D}(t) &= \mathcal{D}_0 = \text{const.} > 0, \\
\dot{\theta}(t) &= \dot{\theta}_0 = \text{const.} \neq 0, \\
z(t) &= z_0 = 0,
\end{aligned}
\right\}
$$

where we also have that

$$\mathcal{D}_0 \dot{\theta}_0^2 = \left(\frac{\partial V}{\partial \mathcal{D}}\right)_{\mathcal{D} = \mathcal{D}_0}.$$

We now introduce, into the equations, the expressions

$$
\left.
\begin{aligned}
\mathcal{D} &= \mathcal{D}_0 + \delta\mathcal{D}, \\
\theta &= \theta_0 + \delta\theta, \\
z &= \delta z,
\end{aligned}
\right\}
$$

for a motion in a neighbouring orbit, and neglect all terms whose order in the variations δ exceeds the first. It follows that

$$
\left.
\begin{aligned}
(\delta\mathcal{D})^{\cdot\cdot} - \dot{\theta}_0^2 \delta\mathcal{D} - 2\mathcal{D}_0\dot{\theta}_0\,\delta\theta &= -\left(\frac{\partial^2 V}{\partial \mathcal{D}^2}\,\delta\mathcal{D} + \frac{\partial^2 V}{\partial \mathcal{D}\,\partial z}\,\delta z\right)_0, \\
2\dot{\theta}_0(\delta\mathcal{D})^{\cdot} + \mathcal{D}_0(\delta\theta)^{\cdot} &= 0, \\
(\delta z)^{\cdot\cdot} &= -\left(\frac{\partial^2 V}{\partial z\,\partial \mathcal{D}}\,\delta\mathcal{D} + \frac{\partial^2 V}{\partial z^2}\,\delta z\right)_0.
\end{aligned}
\right\}
$$

(The suffix 0 simply denotes that the values are attained on the circle $\mathcal{D} = \mathcal{D}_0, z = 0$.)

Now the component of the field intensity in the z-direction vanishes on $z = 0$, for reasons of symmetry. It then follows from

$$\frac{\partial V}{\partial z} = 0, \quad \text{for} \quad z = 0 \quad \text{and all } \mathscr{D},$$

that

$$\frac{\partial^2 V}{\partial \mathscr{D} \, \partial z} = 0 \quad \text{for} \quad \mathscr{D} = \mathscr{D}_0, \quad z = 0.$$

The system of the three linear differential equation for $\delta\mathscr{D}$, $\delta\theta$ and δz now separates into two independent sub-systems, namely

$$\left. \begin{array}{r} (\delta\mathscr{D})^{\cdot\cdot} + \left\{ \left(\dfrac{\partial^2 V}{\partial \mathscr{D}^2} \right)_0 - \dot{\theta}_0^2 \right\} \delta\mathscr{D} - 2\mathscr{D}_0 \dot{\theta}_0 \, \delta\theta = 0, \\[2mm] 2\dot{\theta}_0 (\delta\mathscr{D})^{\cdot} + \mathscr{D}_0 (\delta\theta)^{\cdot} = 0, \end{array} \right\}$$

and

$$(\delta z)^{\cdot\cdot} + \left(\frac{\partial^2 V}{\partial z^2} \right)_0 \delta z = 0.$$

The motion in the central plane is thus independent of the motion perpendicular to it.

Let us consider, first of all, the second equation. The double derivative $(\partial^2 V / \partial z^2)_0$ was denoted by γ in § 2.4, and we found there a method by which its value could be determined observationally, for the part of the Galaxy near the Sun. It is obvious that γ is positive. We see, on substitution, that the function $\alpha e^{\lambda t}$ is a solution of the equation, where α is an arbitrary constant and λ a solution of the equation

$$\lambda^2 + \gamma = 0.$$

This equation has the two imaginary roots $\pm \sqrt{-\gamma}$, and the differential equation the two independent solutions $e^{+\sqrt{(-\gamma)}\,t}$ and $e^{-\sqrt{(-\gamma)}\,t}$. Every linear combination

$$\alpha e^{+\sqrt{(-\gamma)}\,t} + \beta e^{-\sqrt{(-\gamma)}\,t}$$

evidently satisfies the equation as well. We are only interested in real solutions. Using Euler's theorem

$$e^{\pm\sqrt{(-\gamma)}\,t} = \cos\sqrt{(\gamma)}\,t \pm \sqrt{(-1)} \sin\sqrt{(\gamma)}\,t,$$

we can, with a slightly different meaning of the symbols α and β, write this two-parameter family of solutions in the form

$$\delta z = \alpha \cos\sqrt{(\gamma)}\,t + \beta \sin\sqrt{(\gamma)}\,t.$$

The coefficients α and β are determined so as to fulfil the initial conditions

$$\delta z = \delta_0 z, \quad \delta \dot{z} = \delta_0 \dot{z}, \quad \text{when} \quad t = 0.$$

The final solution is

$$\delta z = \delta_0 z \cos \sqrt{(\gamma)}\, t + \frac{\delta_0 \dot{z}}{\sqrt{\gamma}} \sin \sqrt{(\gamma)}\, t.$$

The pair of equations for $\delta \mathscr{D}$ and $\delta \dot{\theta}$ can be treated correspondingly. We introduce, first of all, the "particular solutions"

$$\delta \mathscr{D} = \alpha e^{\lambda t}, \quad \delta \dot{\theta} = \beta e^{\lambda t},$$

and obtain a homogeneous linear set of equations for α and β, namely

$$\left. \begin{aligned} \left\{ \lambda^2 - \dot{\theta}_0^2 + \left(\frac{\partial^2 V}{\partial \mathscr{D}^2} \right)_0 \right\} \alpha - 2 \mathscr{D}_0\, \dot{\theta}_0 \beta &= 0, \\ 2 \dot{\theta}_0 \lambda \alpha + \mathscr{D}_0 \lambda \beta &= 0. \end{aligned} \right\}$$

The second equation may, in general, be divided by λ without further thought, for the case $\lambda = 0$ corresponds to constant functions $\delta \mathscr{D}$ and $\delta \dot{\theta}$, which satisfy the equations of motion in exceptional cases only. Elimination of the constants α and β leads to the condition that λ fulfil

$$\lambda^2 = -\left(\frac{\partial^2 V}{\partial \mathscr{D}^2} \right)_0 - 3 \dot{\theta}_0^2$$

$$= -\left(\frac{\partial^2 V}{\partial \mathscr{D}^2} + \frac{3}{\mathscr{D}} \frac{\partial V}{\partial \mathscr{D}} \right)_0 .$$

If the right-hand side is negative we can write, as in the case of δz,

$$\left. \begin{aligned} \delta \mathscr{D} &= \alpha_1 \cos |\lambda|\, t + \beta_1 \sin |\lambda|\, t, \\ \delta \theta &= \alpha_2 \cos |\lambda|\, t + \beta_2 \sin |\lambda|\, t, \end{aligned} \right\}$$

and find the coefficients α_1, β_1, α_2 and β_2 from the initial conditions

$$\left. \begin{aligned} \delta \mathscr{D} = \delta_0 \mathscr{D}, \quad & \delta \dot{\mathscr{D}} = \delta_0 \Pi, \\ \delta \theta = \delta_0 \theta, \quad & \delta \dot{\theta} = \frac{\delta_0 \Theta}{\mathscr{D}_0}, \quad \text{for} \quad t = 0. \end{aligned} \right\}$$

In order to study some properties of the orbit we shall find, instead of $\delta\dot\theta$, its time integral $\delta\theta$ (the two quantities have similar forms). Let $\delta_0\Theta$ be the difference between the actual Θ velocity component and the circular velocity at time $t = 0$. Then

$$\left.\begin{aligned}
\delta\mathscr{D} &= \delta_0\mathscr{D}\cos|\lambda|\,t + \frac{\delta_0\Pi}{|\lambda|}\sin|\lambda|\,t, \\[2ex]
\delta\theta &= \delta_0\theta\cos|\lambda|\,t + \frac{\delta_0\Theta}{\mathscr{D}_0|\lambda|}\sin|\lambda|\,t.
\end{aligned}\right\}$$

We now choose cartesian coordinates (ξ_1, ξ_2), rotating with the angular velocity $\dot\theta_0$, in such a way that an element of mass on the circular orbit always has the coordinates $\xi_1 = \mathscr{D}, \xi_2 = 0$. The coordinates of neighbouring elements are then

$$\xi_1(t) = \mathscr{D}_0 + \delta\mathscr{D}, \quad \xi_2(t) = \mathscr{D}_0\,\delta\theta.$$

We fix the origin of time at an instant when the periodic function $\xi_1(t)$ assumes its maximum value, and have

$$\dot\xi_1(0) = \delta_0\Pi = 0,$$

and therefore $\xi_1 = \mathscr{D}_0 + \delta_0\mathscr{D}\cos|\lambda|\,t.$

It then follows, from the second equation of motion

$$2\dot\theta_0(\delta\mathscr{D})^{\cdot} + \mathscr{D}_0(\delta\theta)^{\cdot\cdot} = 0,$$

that $(\delta\theta)^{\cdot\cdot} = 0$ as well, for $t = 0$, so that $\delta_0\theta = 0$ and

$$\xi_2 = \frac{\delta_0\Theta}{|\lambda|}\sin|\lambda|\,t.$$

On elimination of t from the equations for $\xi_1(t)$ and $\xi_2(t)$ we find that the element moves in an ellipse relative to the rotating set of axes, and that the centre of the ellipse coincides at all times with an element of mass moving in a circular orbit.

Systems with spherical symmetry can be treated in a similar way, for, fundamentally, we are only trying to give an approximate description of a very special type of rosette orbits—those which are almost circular.

We finally consider the Galactic System, and make use of § 2.9, where $f(\mathscr{D})$ denoted the gradient of the potential and

$f'(\mathscr{D})$ its derivative. In particular we had the formulae

$$\left(\frac{\partial V}{\partial \mathscr{D}}\right)_0 = f(\mathscr{D}_0), \quad \left(\frac{\partial^2 V}{\partial \mathscr{D}^2}\right)_0 = f'(\mathscr{D}_0),$$

for the present position of the Sun, and consequently

$$\lambda^2 = -\left\{ f'(\mathscr{D}_0) + \frac{3}{\mathscr{D}_0} f(\mathscr{D}_0) \right\}.$$

We also derived there the relations

$$\left. \begin{aligned} \frac{1}{\mathscr{D}_0} f(\mathscr{D}_0) &= (A - B)^2, \\ f'(\mathscr{D}_0) &= -(A - B)(3A + B), \end{aligned} \right\}$$

A and B being Oort's constants. It follows that

$$\lambda^2 = 4B(A - B),$$

which is, in fact, negative. The corresponding period is

$$\frac{2\pi}{|\lambda|} = \frac{\pi}{\sqrt{(|B|\,|A - B|)}};$$

its ratio to the period $2\pi/(A - B)$ of the circular motion (cf. § 2.7) is

$$\frac{1}{2}\sqrt{\left(1 + \left|\frac{A}{B}\right|\right)} \approx 0{\cdot}8.$$

12. Lindblad has investigated the stability of circular motions in stationary, homogeneous distributions of material with rotational symmetry. (Owing to their homogeneity these are not "models" in our sense, for the assumed uniformity of the density is not compatible with the existence of a frequency function.) It was Lindblad's intention to explain the formation of the spiral shapes of nebulae by the instabilities of systems with rotational symmetry. A particular motion is here said to be stable if every initially neighbouring motion remains so for all time. The method consists of a study of the linearized equations of motion, with initial conditions which are close to those of a circular motion. The motion is unstable if λ^2 is positive; it is stable otherwise.

It is found that all circular motions are stable in reasonably flattened systems; however, the outermost motions in the equatorial planes of very strongly flattened systems are unstable. The limit occurs at a ratio of 1 : 3 between the axes, and this corresponds to the most extreme flattening found in the elliptic galaxies. It is, however, rather doubtful whether the agreement remains when the assumed uniform density is replaced by another which tallies better with the actual conditions. For example, all circular motions are stable in a gravitational field due to one mass point only—as is easily verified.

Spiral systems would have to rotate with the ends of their arms preceding if Lindblad's explanation were correct. The question has, admittedly, not yet been finally settled, but it does seem that, in fact, the rotation is in the opposite sense (cf. I, § 5.2). Further, the occurrence of interstellar material in spiral galaxies, and its absence in elliptical galaxies, seem to show that the spiral systems are in an earlier stage of evolution—if one assumes that there is any genetical connexion at all between them.

The origin of the spiral systems is an unsolved problem as yet. Doubtless the interstellar material plays a major part in it. Therefore the methods described in our book seem to be insufficient for a solution.

5. The complete set of basic equations

1. Only stationary models have been treated so far. This was quite natural, for the energy integral, which is essential in our calculation, exists only when the potential is time independent. If the system has rotational or spherical symmetry, the area integral exists even when the potential is time dependent. This fact follows at once from the working of § 3.2. It is, however, impossible to construct a reasonable frequency function from the area integral only, since, for example, it would not contain all the velocity components. Non-stationary models can therefore not be found in this way.

It was thought, for some time, that a certain transformation of space and time could be used to make a non-stationary model correspond to every stationary one. Further study showed, however, that a uniform density distribution is a necessary consequence of such a correspondence, and this implies a very great restriction on the applicability of the method. We shall return to this question in Section 9.

The reason that the defect of these models was not found at once was that Liouville's equation had been treated in isolation, Poisson's equation being ignored. Only after the inclusion of the latter was the number of reasonable solutions reduced almost to zero. All the necessary conditions must be considered simultaneously if a useful model is to be found.

This was our method in the previous paragraph, even if it was not formulated explicitly there. The law of conservation of mass enters into Liouville's equation as well as into the equation

$$\rho = \int_{\Gamma_u} f \mathrm{d}u;$$

Newton's equations of motion also enter into Liouville's equation, and Poisson's equation expresses Newton's law of gravitation. The multiplicity of models was limited by the additional requirement of time-independence.

The latter requirement is now dropped, and we re-formulate our complete set of equations. They are:

Liouville's equation:

$$\frac{\partial f}{\partial t} + \frac{\partial f}{\partial x_j} u_j - \frac{\partial f}{\partial u_j} \frac{\partial V}{\partial x_j} = 0,$$

$$\rho(x, t) = \int_{\Gamma_u} f(u, x, t) \, \mathrm{d}u,$$

Law of gravitation:

$$V(x, t) = G \int_{\Gamma_\xi} \frac{\rho(\xi)}{|x - \xi|} \, \mathrm{d}\xi.$$

In addition there is the initial condition

$$f(u, x, 0) = \overset{o}{f}(u, x),$$

where $\overset{o}{f}$ stands for a given initial distribution. Both $\rho(x, 0)$ and $V(x, 0)$ are evidently determined when $\overset{o}{f}$ is known.

In II, § 4, we asked by what means the evolution of a system could be found. In IV, § 3.1, we referred, as a possible method, to the integration of the particle equations of motion. This way is correct in principle, but completely useless in practice. On the other hand the basic equations of the continuum model, which we have just given, can be used in an actual calculation, valid for a limited interval of time, as will be shown below, and this answers our question of II, § 4.

The description of the motion in the large is, nevertheless, possible only with a particle model. This was discussed in IV, § 1–4. Two related problems, which remain unsolved, are the determination of the initial distributions $\overset{\circ}{f}$ in the real systems and an explanation of their present states.

2. The evolution of a system during a short interval of time is determined, in the first place, by its gravitational potential at time $t = 0$. The change of the potential in the course of time affects the motion of the material only in the second approximation. The frequency function $f(u, x, t)$ can therefore be approximately evaluated, for small $|t|$, in the following way.

The initial density $\rho(x, 0)$ and potential $V(x, 0)$ are found from the initial distribution $f(u, x, 0) = \overset{\circ}{f}(u, x)$. They are then introduced into the Newtonian equations of motion, whose integrals $\phi_i(u, x, t)$ and $\psi_i(u, x, t)$ are determined, with the initial conditions

$$\left.\begin{aligned}\phi_i(u, x, 0) &\equiv u_i, \\ \psi_i(u, x, 0) &\equiv x_i.\end{aligned}\right\}$$

For sufficiently small values of $|t|$, $\overset{\circ}{f}\{\phi(u, x, t), \psi(u, x, t)\}$ is a first approximation to the frequency function $f(u, x, t)$. This is an approximate method of finding the evolution of the system. The quality of the approximation is usually satisfactory, but it may be improved thus.

We regard the initial distribution $\overset{\circ}{f}(u, x)$ as the zeroth approximation $f^{(0)}(u, x, t)$ to the frequency function $f(u, x, t)$. Our method above is a means of finding a first approximation $f^{(1)}(u, x, t)$ from the zeroth approximation. The same method can now be applied to the first approximation to find a second approximation $f^{(2)}(u, x, t)$, and so on. The resulting sequence of functions $f^{(0)}, f^{(1)}, f^{(2)}, \ldots$ converges uniformly to a limiting function f, which is the unique solution of the problem. The formal proof is rather troublesome, and we shall not reproduce it here. The method, as stated, seems very reasonable; basically it is merely a way of adapting the theorem of existence and uniqueness, given in III, § 2.1, to apply to a continuum, or to an infinite number of coordinates.

Once again the solution f for a limited interval of time is continuously dependent on the initial distribution $\overset{\circ}{f}$. If the initial conditions are sufficiently close, the corresponding frequency function can be made arbitrarily close.

3. The last theorem leads to a criterion for the "stability" of stationary models. In contrast to IV, § 3, "stability" is now defined in this way. We consider a system whose initial distribution is close to that of a stationary one, but is otherwise arbitrary. If the initially neighbouring system remains close to the stationary system for all time, the latter is said to be stable.

The problem posed by our definition, which is to find a necessary and sufficient criterion for stability, cannot really be solved rigorously, because the continuum models give no information about evolution in the large. On the other hand such rigorous answers are not required in practical applications. We have seen, in Chapter II, that continuum models describe real stellar systems only for limited intervals of time, since interactions between individual stars are neglected by them. The last theorem of the previous section gives the required answer, for small intervals of time, because it states that models which are neighbours to a stationary state at time $t = 0$ remain so for small enough values of $|t|$.

This is the true justification for the use of stationary models, for an exactly stationary state will never occur in nature. A stationary model would thus be useless if a real system, originally its neighbour, immediately began to diverge from it.

It only remains to estimate the lengths of time for which we can be sure of the applicability of continuum models and of the truth of the neighbourhood theorem; and we shall do so now.

4. There are two problems concerning the conditions under which a real stellar system can be described by a continuum model.

We first seek those properties of a real system which enable us to represent its mechanical state by an initial distribution

$\overset{0}{f}(u,x)$ at any instant $t = 0$. If this is possible we next ask: For how long can the continuum model validly represent the real system?

There is no rigorously exact answer to our first problem. We must use our physical insight, which alone can bridge the gap between the discrete and the continuous, though it is possible that modern mathematical statistics will one day reduce the width of the gap.

We introduce dimensionless variables in order to answer the second question. The dimensionless variables are denoted by the superscript $\sim$. We write

$$\left.\begin{array}{l} x_i = x_* \tilde{x}_i, \\[4pt] u_i = x_* \sqrt{(G\rho_*)}\,\tilde{u}_i, \\[4pt] t = t_*\tilde{t}, \quad \text{where} \quad t_* = \dfrac{1}{\sqrt{(G\rho_*)}}; \end{array}\right\}$$

$$\left.\begin{array}{l} f(u,x,t) = \dfrac{1}{x_*^3\sqrt{(G\rho_*)}}\tilde{f}(\tilde{u},\tilde{x},\tilde{t}), \\[4pt] V(x,t) = x_*^2 G\rho_* \tilde{V}(\tilde{x},\tilde{t}), \\[4pt] \rho(x,t) = \rho_*\tilde{\rho}(\tilde{x},\tilde{t}). \end{array}\right\}$$

The symbol x_* stands for a typical length of the model, say its diameter, and ρ_* for a typical density, say its mean density at time $t = 0$.

When these expressions are introduced into the three basic equations there result the corresponding equations for the dimensionless variables, with the dimensionless constant of gravitation $\tilde{G} = 1$. To every dimensionless solution $\tilde{f}(\tilde{u},\tilde{x},\tilde{t})$ there corresponds a family of ∞^2 dimensional solutions $f(u,x,t)$, simply derived from $\tilde{f}$ by transformations of scale. All this is analogous to the scale transformations for particle systems, which were treated in IV, § 5.1.

In particular we obtain once more a natural time scale

$$t_* = \frac{1}{\sqrt{(G\rho_*)}},$$

substantially in agreement with the previous scale, provided ρ_* is identified with the mean initial density.

The development of a stellar system can thus be said to be described by the continuum model if f, or rather $\tilde{f}$, is a useful approximation for a period whose corresponding dimensionless magnitude is at least of order unity. In any other case the model ceases to apply immediately after the origin of time. Hence if a continuum model gives a useful description of a stellar system at all, it does so for an interval at least of order

$$t_* \approx \frac{1\cdot5 \times 10^7}{\sqrt{\rho_*}} \text{ [years],}$$

the density being measured in solar masses per cubic parsec. This statement is exact, in fact almost a tautology. There are still two points to discuss.

Firstly, what are the conditions which make the application of this model reliable? A plausible answer, based on considerations of continuity, seems to be that the reliability is assured for particle systems whose initial states are represented, in sufficient approximation, by a continuous initial distribution $\overset{\circ}{f}(u, x)$.

The second point is that we have simply taken ρ_* to be the mean initial density. We could equally well have chosen the maximum initial density—or one, say, 10^{20} times as large—or one smaller by such a factor. Why is the mean density chosen?

Let us introduce the dimensionless variables into the equations of motion

$$\ddot{x}_i = -\frac{\partial V}{\partial x_i}$$

$$= -G \frac{\partial}{\partial x_i} \int_{\Gamma_y} \frac{\rho(y, t)}{|y - x|} \, dy.$$

The magnitudes of the dimensionless accelerations are then of the order unity, when ρ_* stands for the mean density—with only quite artificial exceptions. A star therefore requires a time of order t_* to traverse the system. The continuum model will probably remain valid for such a length of time.

This lower bound is not very sensitive to the exact value of the mean density. For stellar systems in general it is of the order of 10^8 years, and therefore rather small when compared with the cosmical time-scale, which is the time scale of the system of stellar systems. According to the same formula, the value of the latter is about 10^9 or 10^{10} years. The continuum model probably describes the stellar systems for a multiple of their respective time scales, probably for a period of the order of 10^9 years.

5. According to § 2.1 the set of hydrodynamical equations is

$$
\left.
\begin{aligned}
&\frac{\partial \rho}{\partial t} = -\frac{\partial}{\partial x_j}(\rho \bar{u}_j), \\
&\frac{\partial \bar{u}_i}{\partial t} = -\frac{\partial \bar{u}_i}{\partial x_j}\bar{u}_j - \frac{\partial V}{\partial x_i} - \frac{1}{\rho}\frac{\partial}{\partial x_j}\{\rho(\overline{u_i - \bar{u}_i})(u_j - \bar{u}_j)\}, \\
&V = G\int_{\Gamma_y} \frac{\rho(y, t)}{|y - x|}\,\mathrm{d}y.
\end{aligned}
\right\}
$$

This set also seems to be valid for a period of unit dimensionless order of magnitude. As we pointed out in § 2.3, the set is incomplete, for there are no equations dealing with the stress tensor. The latter is best treated as a time-independent function given by the initial distribution. The approximation is useful for a period of order unity, and is better than that given in § 2.3, where, in addition, the potential was assumed to remain constant.

6. There are mechanical determinations of the so-called "age of the universe", although the term is rather bold. The periods of time concerned are, in fact, significant in the evolution of stellar systems, or of the system of stellar systems, but only in the sense that non-stationary systems undergo considerable mechanical changes during them. The determinations usually yield values at least of order t_*. We can now understand the reason for this, for we have seen that every significant change of the system requires a time of this order.

7. In addition to the dynamical time scale t_* there is a kinematic scale $1/K$ in the mechanical theory of the system of stellar systems (cf. IV, § 5.6, and V, § 2.5). K is the (approximately) constant ratio of the radial velocity R and the distance r. Both scales are of the order of 10^9–10^{11} years, and this seems to justify the interpretation, as a Doppler effect, of the red shift in the

spectra of the galaxies. We have always used this interpretation, although we mentioned the objection in I, § 5.3, that the range of hypothetical velocities extends almost to the speed of light. Mechanics therefore appears to show that we must expect motions rapid enough to correspond to the observed line shifts; neverthe-less this is true only in order of magnitude. It is by no means impossible that there should be other physical effects, causing further shifts of the same order to the red or to the violet, without our being able to distinguish them from the kinematic red shifts, for order of magnitude plus the same order of magnitude still equals the same order of magnitude. We can say nothing about such possible physical effects; however, there are good dynamical reasons for believing in the existence of motions corresponding to the red shifts.

8. The scale-transformations also lead to estimates of mass. We use the term "const" to denote a dimensionless, positive constant depending only on the model. The total mass M of any system then satisfies

$$M = \text{const.} x_*^3 \rho_*$$

$$= \text{const.} \frac{x_*^3}{G t_*^2},$$

so that

$$M = \text{const.} \frac{x_* u_*^2}{G},$$

where

$$u_* = \frac{x_*}{t_*}$$

is a characteristic (dimensional) speed, say the dispersion of the observed radial velocities.

The factor of proportionality is usually to be found by means of the dimensionless fundamental equations, but occasionally a simpler estimate can be made. Suppose that we have two systems with a similar structure (i.e. with equal dimensionless distribu-tion functions), and suppose that the values of M_*, u_* and x_* are known for one of them. The factor of proportionality can then be evaluated, and from it an estimate made for the mass of the second system. An example is the case of the open star clusters and the clusters of galaxies. (The analogy is not quite perfect, since the open clusters cannot really be said to be mechanically closed systems.)

The factor of proportionality is of order unity, as a rule; this may be seen at once from the dimensionless fundamental equations. This value may be used when there is none available which seems to be better.

9. In Section I we mentioned the space-time transformation, by means of which a non-stationary model could, apparently, be made to correspond to every stationary one, and we shall briefly discuss this problem here.

The impulse for this work was given by Chandrasekhar's study of non-stationary models. He considered distribution functions of the form $f(Q)$, where

$$Q = a_{ij}(x,t)\{u_i - \bar{u}_i(x,t)\}\{u_j - \bar{u}_j(x,t)\} + \psi(x,t),$$

and introduced this expression into Liouville's equation. The left-hand side becomes a third-order polynomial in the u_i variables, all whose coefficients must vanish. There follows a set of ten partial differential equations for the ten functions

$$\psi(x,t), \quad \bar{u}_i(x,t), \quad a_{ij}(x,t).$$

Chandrasekhar succeeded in finding a class of particular solutions for this set after some very troublesome calculations. He did not use Poisson's equation in his investigation.

Schürer subsequently arrived at apparently even more general results in a brief and simple manner. He introduced new co-ordinates ξ_i and a new time variable τ into the equations of motion

$$\ddot{x}_i = -\frac{\partial}{\partial x_i}V(x)$$

by writing
$$x_i(t) = \frac{\xi_i(\tau)}{\phi(\tau)},$$
$$\frac{d\tau}{dt} = \{\phi(\tau)\}^2.$$

Here $\phi(\tau)$ is some function of the time variable τ. The transformed equations of motion then read

$$\left.\begin{array}{l}
\dfrac{d^2\xi_i}{d\tau^2} = -\dfrac{\partial}{\partial\xi_i}\,\Omega(\xi,\tau), \\[2ex]
\Omega(\xi,\tau) = -\dfrac{1}{2}\dfrac{1}{\phi}\dfrac{d^2\phi}{d\tau^2}\cdot\xi_j\,\xi_j + \dfrac{1}{\phi^2}V(\xi/\phi),
\end{array}\right\}$$

and may be regarded as the equations of motion of a non-stationary model with the potential $\Omega(\xi,\tau)$. The known first integrals of the stationary model are converted into first integrals of the non-stationary model by means of the transformation. The distribution function can then be constructed in terms of these known integrals.

Schürer, in his turn, also neglected Poisson's equation, which, if it is taken into account, requires that all the possible models have a density constant in the whole space Γ_x. Their total mass is therefore infinite, or else their density zero. Such models are not useful in general, but there is one exception: Systems with spherical symmetry possessing an (almost) homogeneous nucleus can be described, approximately, and for a limited period, by the appropriate model. The structure of the outer shell will only influence the evolution of the nucleus when its elements begin to penetrate there. The time when this happens is the later the smaller is the dispersion of velocities. In the limiting case, where the velocity spread vanishes, we recover the hydrodynamical model, mentioned in § 2.4, which, in turn, is the continuous analogue of the particle model of IV, § 5.6.

A much simpler model, apparently due to Boltzmann, may be used in this one application. It corresponds to the special case of Chandrasekhar's function

$$\left.\begin{array}{l}
f = f(Q), \\[1ex]
Q = (\phi u_j - \dot\phi x_j)(\phi u_j - \dot\phi x_j), \\[1ex]
\phi = \phi(t).
\end{array}\right\}$$

The density is at once found to be

$$\rho(x,t) = \frac{\rho_0}{\phi^3}, \quad \rho_0 = \text{const.},$$

and, owing to the spherical symmetry, the potential is

$$V(x,t) = \frac{2\pi}{3}\, G\, \frac{\rho_0}{\phi^3}\, x_j x_j.$$

If these functions are substituted into Liouville's equation it is found that

$$\ddot{\phi} = -\frac{4\pi}{3}\frac{G\rho_0}{\phi^2};$$

this is the same equation as we derived for the function $s(t)$ in IV, § 5.6. Further discussion of it seems superfluous.

10. We close with a description of an exact calculation of a non-stationary stellar system. If the initial distribution $\overset{\circ}{f}$ is analytic, the frequency function f can be found by means of a power series expansion in all the variables, which is introduced, into the basic equations, with undetermined coefficients. The equations and the initial conditions determine the coefficients uniquely. The convergence of the method has not been studied yet, but the first terms should yield useful approximations for small $|t|$, say for $|\tilde{t}| < 1$.

This method is troublesome in practice. On the other hand the main method of successive approximations, described in § 5.2, leads quite readily to a first approximation, when the necessary quadratures are estimated. Such simplifications diminish the accuracy of the result, so that the power series method is more reliable.

Both methods have been applied to the initial distribution

$$\overset{\circ}{f}(u,x) = \text{const.} \exp\ [ax_j x_j - b u_j u_j],$$

which has spherical symmetry; a and b are two positive constants. It was assumed that a is a very small number, so that the density was initially almost uniform over a large volume of position space Γ_x. The main results found were as follows.

In the beginning the system contracts slowly; later it does so faster. It becomes less and less uniform, in that there is a rapid increase of the density at the centre, as well as of the density gradient in its vicinity. The system passes through an instant of greatest concentration and then expands again. The mean radial velocity $\bar{R}(r, t)$, which initially pointed inwards, now points outwards. The reversal of the flow does not occur at the same instant at all points, but happens earlier the more distant from the centre is the point considered. The velocity surfaces, which were spherical initially, undergo deformations.

It was the purpose of this model to explain the formation of the globular clusters. We have mentioned (in IV, § 4.5) why it does not happen this way. We now conclude our report on the continuum models and shall only add a brief summary of the principal results.

6. Summary

The frequency function is the fundamental concept of stellar dynamics, that is, of the theory of the continuum models. It is defined as the mass density of the model in a six-dimensional phase space Γ, which is the Cartesian product of the ordinary (position) space Γ_x and the corresponding velocity space Γ_u. The flow of material in Γ is determined by a set of six differential equations, identical with the set of Newtonian equations of motion for a particle of unit mass in a given potential field. The flow does not affect the mass of the moving material: the mass frequency, or the frequency function of the model, is therefore a first integral of the equations of motion and satisfies Liouville's equation (§ 1).

By means of certain integrations over velocity space we deduced, from Liouville's equation, the equation of continuity and a generalization of Euler's equations for the mass density $\rho(x, t)$ and velocity $\bar{u}_i(x, t)$ of flow in the position space Γ_x. But it seems impossible to give a reliable "equation of state" for the material of the system; the set of basic equations is thus incomplete and of limited use only. A kinematic point of view is found to be more fruitful than a dynamic one, particularly when dealing with our Galactic system or with the system of galaxies.

A more detailed model describing our Galaxy, which is assumed to be stationary, is derived from its frequency function, which we express suitably in terms of the energy and the area integrals. These two integrals are also available for the frequency functions of stationary systems with spherical symmetry (§ 3).

Poisson's equation is also needed for a complete calculation of such a model. The frequency function is expressed in terms of the known first integrals and is integrated over all velocity space, to give the mass density in position space as a function of the potential and the radius vector. The density is then substituted into Poisson's equation, which is solved for the potential. If the total mass of the model is to be finite, the energies of all the elements of mass must be uniformly bounded. But even when they are so bounded, this still does not imply the finiteness of the total mass, although a very small change in the distribution function will ensure it. All the models have shells with almost polytropic structures. By far the largest number of elements of mass describe rosette-like orbits about the centre point. Corresponding studies of stationary models with rotational symmetry are still in their infancy. One can say little more than that the energies of the elements of mass must be uniformly bounded if the system is to have finite dimensions (§ 4).

The continuum model has a complete set of basic equations, comprising Liouville's and Poisson's equations, and the relation between the density and the distribution function. If an initial distribution is also given, the equations can be used to trace the evolution for a period roughly equal to the natural time scale. The latter can be found by the introduction of dimensionless variables into the basic equations. It is safe to assume that the continuum model is applicable for this length of time, even though it does neglect the possibility of close encounters of stars, and their effect on the evolution of the system. Stationary models will likewise be stable during such periods (§ 5).

Examples

1. According to its definition, in § 1.2, it is always possible to express the frequency function as an analytical function, particularly in the case of stationary systems with spherical symmetry. (Why?) This is not possible according to § 4.4. Do we have a contradiction here?

2. What is the mathematical content of the proof of the fundamental theorem in § 1.4? Is the method logically free from objection?

3. Use the energy integral E_3 to derive the density law of § 2.4 from the exponential formula of § 3.4.

4. Construct, in all its details, the cosmological model mentioned in § 2.4. State, in particular, the special hypotheses used. How must the model be changed when the hypotheses are generalized?

5. Why do the vectors e_i, e_i', e_i'', of § 2.5, form an orthogonal triad?

6. Generalize the work of § 2.7 to the three-dimensional case.

7. Calculate the second-order terms for the kinematic theory of § 2.5.

8. Show that Liouville's equation is plausible by means of the following "local" argument (in contrast to the "substantial" argument in the text). For every element of volume in phase space Γ, the rate of increase of mass equals the rate of inflow of material across its boundary.

9. Express the potential V in terms of the density ρ, in the differential equation of the isothermal gas sphere. Show that the resulting equation has a solution of the form const. r^{-2}. Does this prove the theorem, mentioned in § 3.2, concerning the behaviour at infinity of $\rho(r)$? Is the theorem proved if it can be shown that the equation has an "asymptotic solution" of the form

$$\frac{a_2}{r^2} + \frac{a_3}{r^3} + \frac{a_4}{r^4} + \dots ?$$

10. Suppose that $f(E - k^2 F)$, with $k > 0$, is any given positive function which is "smooth" and decreases towards zero. Let it define a model with spherical symmetry, which is now calculated according to the method of § 4.1 to 100,000 places, by means of a computing machine (yet to be built). The mass function $m(r)$, in particular, is determined. What is the character of the approximate function for $m(r)$? Is there a contradiction here with the corresponding theorem of § 4.4?

11. There are asymptotic solutions of the differential equation for the polytropic gas sphere. Are they significant for stellar dynamics?

12. A formula of § 4.5 gives the total mass of a polytropic gas sphere. Determine the factor of proportionality which is missing there.

13. Construct a polytropic gas sphere with a sharp boundary, i.e. a boundary where the density gradient differs from zero.

14. Let $T(r)$ be the orbital period of an element of mass moving along a circle about the centre of a stationary system with spherical symmetry. Discuss the behaviour of the function $T(r)$ when the mass density decreases monotonically with increasing radial distance r. Consider, in particular, the case when r is small.

15. Are there circular orbits near the boundary of stationary systems, which have spherical symmetry and a finite radius? What is the form of those orbits which reach the edge?

16. Investigate Lindblad's stability condition of § 4.11 for a potential of the form

$$V = \frac{a}{\mathscr{D}^\mu} + \frac{b}{r^\nu}.$$

17. The following has been proved: If there is a solution of the basic equations which is stationary, has rotational symmetry and an ellipsoidal velocity distribution, and if one assumes that there is an asymptotic expansion of such a solution, then all the coefficients in the expansion vanish. Can one deduce, therefore, that neither the corresponding solutions, nor the corresponding systems, really exist?

M

18. Compare the properties of the models, given in § 5.9 and § 5.10, for non-stationary systems with spherical symmetry.

19. Determine the time-dependent integral obtained from the energy integral by means of Schürer's transformation in § 5.9. Why is the transform of an integral also an integral?

20. Let the "time average" $\hat{f}$ of the frequency function f be defined by

$$\hat{f}(u, x) = \lim_{T \to \infty} \frac{1}{2T} \int_{-T}^{T} f(u, x, t) \, dt.$$

Does $\hat{f}$ satisfy an equation of Liouville's type without a time-dependent term, even when f is time-dependent? In particular, consider a distribution function which is periodic in time, such as

$$f(u, x, t) = f_0(u, x) + \sum_{1}^{\infty} \{f_r(u, x) \cos rt + g_r(u, x) \sin rt\},$$

and use it to show that the answer to this question is in the negative.

Comments and References to the Literature

§ **1.3.** The equations of motion in continuum mechanics cannot be rigorously derived from the particle equations of motion. One can only use physical arguments, or draw conclusions from analogies between the two cases.

§ **2.3.** Lindblad has attempted to explain the spiral structure of the galaxies by means of the hydrodynamical equations, in the following way. He considered a stationary system in rotation, and studied its stability (in the sense of § 5.3). To this end he formed the corresponding linear variational equations and tried to show that their eigen-solutions—represented formally by Fourier series—are stable under certain conditions and unstable under others. Spiral arms are supposed to be formed in the latter case. The theory demands a considerable effort formally, but still seems to require further mathematical clarification. For this reason we have not discussed it in greater detail in the text, and, in any case, it was not our intention to make such criticisms in this book. Chandrasekhar [27] gives references, and Coutrez gives a very readable summary in:

[28] COUTREZ, R., *Annales de l'Observatoire Royale de Belgique*, Troisième Série, tome IV.

Lindblad has also tried to give a better justification for a polytropic relation between the pressure and density in the Galactic System, cf.:

[29] LINDBLAD, B., On a theorem in the dynamics of stellar systems, *Stockholms Observatoriums Annaler*, **16**, 1–34, 1950.

§ **2.4.** See also:

[30] OORT, J. H., *B.A.N.*, **6**, 249, 1932.

The application of the hydrodynamical equations to cosmology is extensively treated by:

[31] HECKMANN, O., *Theorien der Kosmologie*, Berlin, 1942.

This may be compared with:

[32] KURTH, R., Ueber den Zusammenhang zwischen dynamischer Kosmologie und Stellardynamik, *Z. Astrophys.*, **28**, 1–16, 1950.

§ 2.5. The terms of the second order may be found, for example, in Smart's book [5].

§ 2.6. In the text we have assumed the observable part of Universe to be so small a region around our Galaxy that the functions may be represented linearly. Is this, in fact, permissible? A possible objection might be that radial velocities are observed up to one-fifth the speed of light c. If one regards c as the highest possible speed, one may rightly doubt whether distances can be said to be small when they correspond to values of the radial velocity, which are comparable with their upper limit. The fact that the proportionality of $\dot{r}$ to r is still observed at such high speeds seems, then, to limit our choice of admissible models—in contradiction to the statement in the text. Observations appear to demand a homogeneous model, like that of Chapter IV, § 5.6, or the model of the general theory of relativity (cf., for example, Heckmann [31]). But we must remember that any possible deviations from proportionality would be hard to detect. We might have, for example, that

$$r = r(\dot{r}) = \frac{1}{K}\left\{1 + \alpha_1\left(\frac{\dot{r}}{c}\right) + \alpha_2\left(\frac{\dot{r}}{c}\right)^2 + \ldots\right\}.$$

The relative errors in the measured values of r would have to be of a smaller order than $\alpha_1(\dot{r}/c) \approx \dot{r}/c \lesssim \frac{1}{5}$, if the deviations were to be detected. Can we be sure that such an accuracy is attained? Besides, the distances r are sometimes determined by means of the proportionality. We must bear that in mind in any discussion.

§ 2.9. The estimate of ζ is given by Smart [5]. For the "local stellar system" see, for example, Becker [1].

§ 3.4. The following observation is called the asymmetry of the stellar motions. If one divides the stars near the Sun into classes according to their speeds, the mean speed of a class is found to be a (possibly linear) function of the square of the deviation $(\sigma_\pi^2 + \sigma_\Theta^2 + \sigma_z^2)$.

This only indicates that the velocity distribution for all the stars is unsymmetrical at large speeds, and so certainly not elliptical. The conclusion is self-evident, once the existence of the high-velocity stars has been established. The effect is probably due simply to the fact that different numbers of high-velocity stars are mixed in with the different classes. The usual theoretical explanations (cf. Smart [5] or v. d. Pahlen [25]) are inadmissible; according to them the distribution function is represented by a sum of terms of Schwarzschild's type, each of the form

$$\text{const.} \exp\left[-\frac{1}{2\sigma^2}(2E - 2k_1 F_2 + k_2 F_3^2 + 2k_3 E_3)\right],$$

and each referring to a certain group of stars. The mean square deviation in a particular group evidently depends on the parameters σ, k_2 and k_3, while the rotational velocity $\overline{\Theta}$ depends on k_1 and k_2. If there were a functional dependence between $\overline{\Theta}$ and the mean square deviation, only the parameter k_2, and not σ, k_1 and k_3, would be able to vary from term to term. There is no justification for this. The difficulty remains if the functional dependence is replaced by a correlation, with σ, k_1 and k_3 as scattering parameters.

§ **4.2.** For the equations of the isothermal gas sphere see Chandrasekhar [27], and, in particular,

[33] EMDEN, R., *Gaskugeln*, Leipzig and Berlin, 1907.

[34] CHANDRASEKHAR, S., *An Introduction to the Study of Stellar Structure*, Chicago, 1939.

Eddington gives a lucid account of the calculation of the potential energy for a polytropic gas sphere:

[35] EDDINGTON, A. S., *The Internal Constitution of the Stars*, Cambridge, 1926.

§ **4.4.** For the missing proof of the theorem concerning the distribution function $f(E + hF^2)$, see:

[36] KURTH, R., *Astronomische Nachrichten*, **282**, 97, 1955.

§ **4.5.** Camm introduced polytropic gas spheres to stellar dynamics, though in quite a different way:

[37] CAMM, G. L., *Monthly Not.*, **112**, 155, 1952.

For the Fowler–Hopf theorem see:

[38] FOWLER, R. H., *Monthly Not.*, **91**, 63, 1930.

[39] HOPF, E., *Monthly Not.*, **91**, 653, 1931.

See also Emden [33] and Chandrasekhar [34].

§ **4.6.** The proof is given by Kurth [36]. An important idea, due to Lindblad, is used in the transition from f^* to f_* (cf. Chandrasekhar [27]). Both E and F have been treated as independent non-negative variables in the definition of $f(E, F)$. However, F is no longer fully independent once the value of E is given. For from

$$\left.\begin{array}{l} E = \tfrac{1}{2}(R^2 + T^2) + V(r), \\ F = rT, \end{array}\right\}$$

it necessarily follows that

$$\tfrac{1}{2}T^2 \leqslant E - V(r),$$

and

$$\tfrac{1}{2}F^2 \leqslant r^2\{E - V(r)\}.$$

It is not clear how this affects the choice of the function $f(E, F)$. There is a twofold difficulty. The condition is in the form of an inequality, and, further, the function which bounds the integral is not itself an integral.

May one conclude from this that f does not depend on F at all? If so, the theory becomes formally much simpler and the range of possibilities is considerably narrowed down.

§ **4.7.** Contopoulos has proved the theorem concerning the magnitude of the angle δ. See:

[40] CONTOPOULOS, G., Beitrag zur Dynamik der Kugelsternhaufen, *Z. Astrophysik*, **35**, 67–73, 1954.

Contopoulos also considers systems of infinite radius where there are hyperbolic as well as rosette-like orbits.

§ **4.8.** For the concept of a single-valued first integral, see Wintner [15].

§ **4.9.** The statement about spherical symmetry is sometimes attributed to Jeans in the literature, and for the proof reference is then made to the eighth chapter of his book:

[41] JEANS, J. H., *Astronomy and Cosmogony*, Cambridge University Press, 1929.

I have not been able to find an appropriate proof there.

Differing answers have been given to the question of whether there really are stationary models with rotational symmetry, ellipsoidal velocity distribution and a finite mass. Camm [42] and Fricke [5] deny their existence, the author [43] affirms it.

[42] CAMM, G. L., The ellipsoidal distribution of stellar velocities, *Monthly Not.*, **101**, 195–215, 1941.

[43] KURTH, R., *Z. Astrophysik*, **26**, 100–136, 1949.

All three authors leave gaps in their proofs. The problem is therefore not yet settled.

§ **4.10.** Lindblad has used this investigation to derive the results of §§ 3 and 4. Fundamentally this is only a specialization of the ideas given there, and we shall not repeat it here.

Contopolous has recently described methods for the calculation of stellar orbits in systems of ellipsoidal structure:

[44] CONTOPOULOS, G., Motions of stars in a nebula, *Publ. Lab. Astron. Univ. Athens*, Ser. II, No. 1, 1956.

§ **4.11.** See Chandrasekhar [27] for an exposition and criticism of Lindblad's theory, which we have mentioned in § 2.3. The origin of spiral systems is also discussed by Chandrasekhar [27], v. d. Pahlen [25], and

[45] CURTIS, H. D., "The Nebulae", in *Handbuch der Astrophysik*, Berlin, 1939.

All these theories contain several simplified mathematical hypotheses, which can hardly be convincingly justified.

§ **5.2.** The proof is given by:

[46] KURTH, R., Das Anfangswertproblem der Stellardynamik, *Z. Astrophysik*, **30**, 213–239, 1952.

Heckmann and Strassl have calculated the first approximation for a very special model and for a volume of space so small that all functions can be represented by linear and quadratic expressions. It was their aim to study the fluctuations of the system about its mean state, which was assumed to be stationary (cf. Example 20). However, such a method is unlikely to yield significant results, since the smallness of the volume considered implies that the corresponding time interval is also small. A stellar system is a unit from which one can take arbitrary slices only with a considerable loss in insight.

[47] HECKMANN, O., and STRASSL, H., Zur Dynamik des Sternsystems, *Veroffentl. Universitats-Sternwarte Göttingen*, No. 41 and 43, 1934.

§ **5.4.** Camm advances the opinion, in [10], that non-stationary systems can be described by means of the continuum model for very great lengths of time. He holds that close encounters of single stars have a negligible influence on the evolution of such a system. There is probably something to be said for this point of view.

§ **5.9.** Cf. Chandrasekhar [27], Kurth [43], as well as:
[48] CHANDRASEKHAR, S., *Ap. J.*, **92**, 441 ff., 1940.
[49] SCHÜRER, M., Beitrag zur Dynamik der Sternsysteme, *A.N.*, **273**, 230–242, 1943.
[50] HECKMANN, O., "Statistische Dynamik von Sternsystemen", in *Naturforschung und Medizin in Deutschland*, 1939–46, Vol. **20**.

§ **5.10.** The example given is treated extensively in [24]. A mathematical theory of the expansion in power series is still missing. Further formal solutions of the basic equations are easily found in the shape of series expansions in powers of $1/r$, which seem, however, to diverge. No investigation has yet been made to decide whether they cannot, even so, be used in a calculation of reasonable models.

CHAPTER VI

STATISTICAL MECHANICS OF STELLAR SYSTEMS

1. We shall now consider the third of the basic methods mentioned in II, § 3, concerning the mechanics of stellar systems.

Statistics may only be used when the concept of a probability can be defined for the problem in question. In the case of a mechanical system of n particles, the probability must be assumed to be a set function which is defined for all measurable sets of the $6n$-dimensional phase-space R^{6n}. (The term "phase-space" has the same meaning as in Chapter IV once again.) The following conditions must be satisfied.

The probability is non-negative and totally additive, i.e. the probability of a sum of a denumerable number of sets without a common point equals the sum of their individual probabilities. The probability is normalized, so that unity is the probability corresponding to the whole of R^{6n}. The probability distribution is, in general, assumed to be time independent.

A concept, which is, in substance, logically equivalent, is that of a probability density with the properties below.

The probability density is a point function defined in R^{6n}; it is non-negative and normalized, so that its integral over the whole of the phase-space R^{6n} has the value unity, and it is a first integral, generally time-independent, of the equations of motion. The last property is, essentially, an immediate consequence of Liouville's theorem (III, § 3.3). For a system must have the same (infinitesimal) probability for all points on its streamline, whose every point determines every other point uniquely. Any one of these "events" (namely that the state of the system is represented by a particular point) is a necessary consequence of any other and so all are equally probable. But Liouville's theorem states that the content of an element of volume remains constant along the streamline, and, therefore, so does the ratio of the probability to the content. The probability density is thus a first integral of the equations of motion. This argument is analogous to that of V, § 1.4, where it was shown that the frequency function of the continuum model is also a first integral. Our argument was more mathematical there, here it is physical.

We deduce, quite generally, that a particular type of mechanical system, defined by the equations of motion, admits of a statistical mechanical treatment if and only if there can be found a non-negative, normalizable first integral of these equations. The integral may then be chosen as a probability density, but there are many other possibilities, since every function of a first integral is another first integral (III, § 2.2).

The problem of finding an integral with the necessary properties is, in effect, equivalent to that of IV, § 2.1, which was to find an invariant subset $J \subset R^{6n}$ with a finite positive measure J. If such a set were known, then a possible first integral would be given by the function

$$\psi(x) = \begin{cases} 1, & \text{when } x \in J, \\ 0, & \text{when } x \in R^{6n} - J, \end{cases}$$

(although it is not differentiable in all R^{6n}). Conversely if $\psi(x)$ is such an integral, then the whole space is a set with the required properties, provided that the "natural measure"

$$m(M) = \int_M \mathrm{d}x$$

of any set M is replaced by an artificial measure

$$m(M) = \int_M \psi \mathrm{d}x$$

(one can easily see that this is permissible in all our work).

We know, however, from IV, § 2.1, that there is no invariant region J known for a Newtonian gravitational potential, and that probably none exists. It follows that there probably is no statistical mechanics of stellar systems.

2. It might be thought that a probability distribution could be constructed in the six-dimensional phase-space Γ of V, § 1.1. A probability density could be defined by dividing the distribution

function by the total mass of the system. This is certainly possible, but only leads to a somewhat different interpretation of the continuum model, which might yield a more convenient formulation but would not produce any new results. In particular, it does not take account of the essential property of a stellar system, namely that it consists of a very large number of gravitating particles.

There have been attempts to include this property by means of Boltzmann's equation of the kinetic theory of gases. The latter has a left-hand side identical with that of Liouville's equation; its right-hand side, however, does not vanish, but is a complicated expression taking account of the interaction of any two stars. It is very questionable whether the new equation is an improvement on that of Liouville. Gravitational forces extend very far, for they decrease only slowly with increasing distances, much more slowly than do the mutual forces between two gas atoms in an elastic collision. For this reason it is hardly permissible to reduce the interaction of a given star with all the others to an interaction with its nearest neighbour only—or possibly with a few close neighbours, which are assumed to be mutually independent. We shall not discuss the method any further.

3. There is a whole series of applications of statistical mechanics to stellar systems. It is said, for instance, that as such a system evolves, its entropy "most probably" increases with time: the system tends to a "statistical equilibrium", which it attains after an interval of the order of the "relaxation time" T. From then onwards it has a "Boltzmann distribution of energy", with an "equipartition of energy".

A system with spherical symmetry should then have the same structure as an "isothermal gas sphere" of "infinitely small density". The process of expansion may be pictured as the "escape of high-velocity stars", and the time of dissolution found by means of the Boltzmann distribution.

Systems in rotation finally acquire a "constant angular velocity". The Galaxy has attained neither the state of "rigid rotation" nor that of "equipartition", and this leads to an estimate of its "age".

The following definition for the relaxation time T is given, for example. It is an interval during which the average change in the kinetic energy of a star equals its average value. All explanations have this in common, that the encounters of a star with other stars have had a marked influence on its motion towards the end of the relaxation period. It therefore cannot be assumed that one may still apply the usual stellar dynamical model of a fluid streaming in the six-dimensional phase-space Γ.

We gave an estimate for a lower bound of this time in V, § 5.4. It certainly has nothing to do with a Boltzmann distribution, which requires that a reasonable probability distribution may be defined in the six-dimensional phase space Γ—and this is not the case. The usual method of calculation employs, simultaneously, the (mutually exclusive) concepts of the particle and the continuum, postulates a uniform and constant density, as well as a Boltzmann distribution of energy (or a Maxwellian distribution of velocities), and considers only the encounters of pairs of stars. The procedure is of very doubtful validity, quite apart even from the cardinal objection that no definition can be given of a sensible probability distribution. The calculation also leads to the questionable result—admittedly in a dubious connexion with the virial theorem—that the more stars there are within a sphere of given radius, the larger is T, and so the smaller the influence of individual encounters.

We shall not study these assertions any further, as they are without any real foundation. For a detailed justification of our claim we refer the reader to the literature, and we may add that the point of view developed above contradicts Hopf's theorems, which were *proved* with the same conditions (IV, § 2). We want emphatically to contradict the widespread view that a stellar system may be compared with a gas. A statistical mechanics of gases is possible only because a gas is contained within a vessel, which is an essential part of the system in any theory. There is no such vessel around a stellar system. The latter's continued existence is ensured by the mutual gravitation of its members and this acts quite differently from a vessel. Its action is indeed so complex, that it has not yet been described mathematically.

Examples

1. Let the probability density for the ith particle in its six-dimensional phase space be given by

$$\mathscr{D}_i(\boldsymbol{r}_i, \dot{\boldsymbol{r}}_i) = \left(\frac{1}{\sigma\sqrt{2\pi}}\right)^3 \left(\frac{1}{\tau\sqrt{2\pi}}\right)^3 \exp\left[-\tfrac{1}{2}(r_i^2/\sigma^2 + \dot{r}_i^2/\tau^2)\right], \quad \sigma, \quad \tau = \text{const} > 0,$$

and the probability density of the whole system in R^{6n} by

$$\prod_{i=1}^{n} \mathscr{D}_i(\boldsymbol{r}_i, \dot{\boldsymbol{r}}_i).$$

Why is this definition not admissible?

2. Why is the probability distribution assumed to be time-independent in general?

3. Discuss more precisely how far the existence of a set function expressing "probability" is in fact equivalent to that of a point function expressing "probability density".

4. The essential difficulty in its definition is the condition that the probability distribution be normalizable. Cannot this condition be simply abandoned?

5. Discuss ways and means of ensuring that the normalization can be carried out. Are they of any value?

6. There are many binary stars in the Galaxy. Studies and calculations, similar to those used in finding the relaxation time, show that it is most unlikely that such pairs have come into being by mutual capture. Does this necessarily follow? Is the capture hypothesis contradicted by Hopf's Second Theorem? Does it have any foundation?

7. Conversely, are there any reasons for supposing that binary systems will tend to dissolve under the gravitational action of the field of stars surrounding them?

Comments on the Literature

The claims, quoted in Section 3, are stated more or less fully at various points in all monographs, e.g. in those of Smart [5], Chandrasekhar [27] and v. d. Pahlen [25]. The author has given a more complete criticism in:

[51] KURTH, R., Gibt es eine statistische Mechanik der Sternsysteme?, *ZAMP*, **6**, 115, 1955.

In order to appreciate how wrong the usual conclusions are, one needs, in the first place, to make oneself familiar with the correct results of statistical mechanics. Present-day literature in physics is not very helpful here. The author knows of only one book which contains an exposition that is both logical and mathematically correct:

[52] KHINCHIN, A. J., *Mathematical Foundations of Statistical Mechanics*, New York, 1949.

CONCLUSION

THREE possible hypotheses were mentioned in Chapter II, and only two are useful. We have tried to compare their advantages and their drawbacks, as for instance in V, § 1.1. The author regrets that he found it necessary to make occasional criticisms. On the other hand he is convinced that our insight can deepen only if we do not abandon ourselves to any illusions. The extent and the reliability of our knowledge are much more modest than we tend to think. There are many problems which are still unresolved—and until they are recognized as such we shall make no progress towards their solution.

There are, in any branch of science, problems of two kinds, those of an essentially mathematical nature and those of a physical character. We have tried to keep both kinds in mind. Among the former type there is the problem of the mechanical evolution of a stellar system in the large (IV, § 3), or that of the existence of stationary continuum models with rotational symmetry (V, § 4.8). Among the unsolved astronomical problems we have that of the mechanical and physical evolution of stellar systems (e.g. the globular clusters—cf. IV, § 4.5), particularly as regards the influence of interstellar material. Another such problem is the explanation of the observed lines of evolution. To gain a significant new insight with any reasonable certainty we must pursue research into both these aspects with equal vigour and with a constant interchange of ideas. Such contact seems to us to be becoming less and less prevalent, and for this reason we have attempted, as best we could, to keep it in being in this book.

HINTS FOR THE EXAMPLES

Chapter I

1. A fraction only of the predicted intensity is observed, depending on the wavelength of the light and the distance and the direction of the star. If the percentage absorption were uniform along any direction, that fraction would be $e^{-\kappa r}$, where κ is a positive constant, which is possibly wavelength dependent, and is called the absorption coefficient of the interstellar material.

4. Interstellar material consists of dust and gas. Discoloration occurs when the absorption coefficient does, in fact, vary with the wavelength.

Chapter III

3. Consider, for example, the pair of differential equations

$$\dot{x} = f(x, y), \quad \dot{y} = g(x, y).$$

Eliminate the time variable (or rather the element dt) by division to find

$$\frac{\mathrm{d}y}{\mathrm{d}x} = \frac{g}{f}.$$

The variable y is no longer a function of x which is necessarily single-valued in the large. The equations may be pictured as describing a field of flow in the (x, y) plane.

7. Compare the ideas in the example with the corresponding ones in the text and pay particular attention to the significance of all the symbols. The appropriate nature of the abbreviations ψ, ψ_i and ϕ_i will then become clear.

9. Consider, say, the particular solution $x = \sin(2\pi t)$, $y = \sin(2\pi\nu t)$. The motion of the system is periodic if ν is rational. If ν is irrational and positive, mark off the angles $\nu, 2\nu, 3\nu, \dots$ on the unit circle. The corresponding points accumulate everywhere on the circle, and, in particular, near the zero point. Hence, for a sufficiently large integral value of t, $y = \sin(2\pi\nu t)$ comes arbitrarily close to its initial value zero again and again.

11. The invariant region J in the (u, x) plane is to be bounded by two neighbouring curves of constant energy.

Chapter IV

5. Place a particle at each vertex (and, if desired, at the centroid) of a regular polyhedron. Now bring up another larger and concentric shell of particles, in such a way that the configuration of particles and forces

remains symmetrical—in particular that all forces pass through the centroid. Finally, choose the radius of the outer shell to make the forces proportional to the distance from the centroid, and so on. The construction can, in fact, be done graphically in the plane case.

Chapter V

8. Let $\mathscr{D}$ be a six-dimensional "velocity vector", with components $\dot{u}_i, \dot{x}_i$, let G be an arbitrary region in Γ and let $\mathbf{ds}$ be the (vectorial) differential of its surface S. Then

$$\frac{\partial}{\partial t} \iint_\Gamma f\,du\,dx + \oint_S (f\mathscr{D}).\,\mathbf{ds} = 0.$$

According to Gauss' theorem,

$$\oint_S (f\mathscr{D}).\,\mathbf{ds} = \iint_G \operatorname{div}(f\mathscr{D})\,du\,dx.$$

On substitution into the previous equation and passage to the limit

$$\frac{\partial f}{\partial t} + \operatorname{div}(f\mathscr{D}) = 0,$$

i.e.

$$\frac{\partial f}{\partial t} + \frac{\partial}{\partial x_i}(f\dot{x}_i) + \frac{\partial}{\partial u_i}(f\dot{u}_i) = 0,$$

or

$$\frac{\partial f}{\partial t} + \frac{\partial}{\partial x_i}(fu_i) - \frac{\partial}{\partial u_i}(fV_i) = 0.$$

Chapter VI

2. Consider why the concept of a probability is introduced at all—and then think how it is to be interpreted in a given system.

5. Remember that real space may possibly have a topological structure different from that of three-dimensional number space. From observation we know nothing about its structure in the large.

INDEX